It's another Quality Book from CGP

This book is for 11-14 year olds.

It contains lots of tricky questions designed to make you sweat — because that's the only way you'll get any better.

It's also got some daft bits in to try and make the whole experience at least vaguely entertaining for you.

What CGP is all about

Our sole aim here at CGP is to produce the highest quality books — carefully written, immaculately presented and dangerously close to being funny.

Then we work our socks off to get them out to you — at the cheapest possible prices.

Published by Coordination Group Publications Ltd.
Illustrated by Sandy Gardner (e-mail: illustrations@sandygardner.co.uk),
Bowser, Colorado USA, Lex Ward and Ashley Tyson

Contributors:
Erik Blakeley
Chris Dennett
Paddy Gannon
Theo Haywood
Ed Lacey
Rachel Selway
Laurence Stamford
Kate Stevens
Jane Towle
Nick White

ISBN: 978 1 84146 248 6
Groovy Website: www.cgpbooks.co.uk
Printed by Elanders Hindson Ltd, Newcastle upon Tyne.
Clipart sources: CorelDRAW® and VECTOR.

Contents

Taken out of the curriculum but still important

A few pages have got a splodge like this one where bits have been taken out of the syllabus. This stuff _shouldn't_ come up in the SATs, but it's still really important so we left it in.

Life Processes and Cells

Q1 The seven life processes are things that all living organisms do.

Write down the seven life processes in the spaces below.

1) ....

2) ....

3) ....

4) ....

5) ....

6) ....

7) ....

Q2 **Below is shown a picture of an animal cell. Label the three main parts of the cell.**

1) ....

2) ....

3) ....

Q3 **A picture of a plant cell is shown below. Label the six main parts of the cell.**

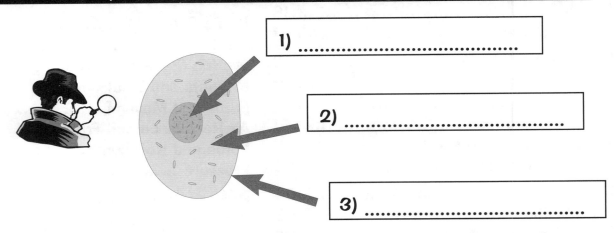

1) ....

2) ....

3) ....

4) ....

5) ....

6) ....

If you're stuck... see Page 1 of our KS3 Revision Guide (Levels 3-6) ☺   *Life Processes and Living Things*

Plant Organs

Q1 Below is shown a picture of a smiley plant. Label its four main organs.

1) ....

2) ....

3) ....

4) ....

Q2 Which of the plant's four main organs contains the reproductive organs?

....

Q3 Which of the plant's four main organs are the organs of photosynthesis?

....

Q4 The roots are important to a plant for several reasons. For example, they take up some of the substances needed for nutrition.

a) What are the two substances that a plant takes in through its roots for nutrition?

....

b) Name another reason why a plant has roots.

....

Q5 What do leaves contain that uses light to change carbon dioxide and water into glucose?

....

4

Specialised Cells and Organs

Q1   This question is about sperm cells. Look at the picture below of a sperm cell.

a)   **What is the purpose of the sperm cell's tail?**

....

....

b)   **What is the name given to the type of information contained in the chromosomes?**

....

c)   **What is the job of the enzymes that are carried in the head of the sperm cell?**

....

....

....

Q2   This question is about root hair cells. Look at the picture below of this type of cell.

Name two things that the root hair cell absorbs for nutrition?

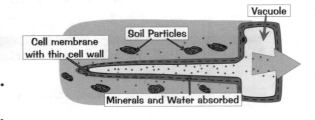

1)   ....

2)   ....

Q3   The following sequence shows how various bits come together to make an organism.

a)   **Label the sequence using the following words: organ, tissue, organism, cell.**

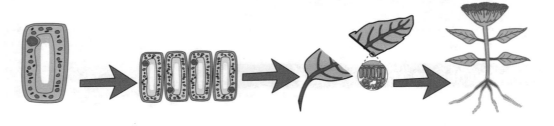

....

b)   **Is it OK to use this sort of sequence for animals as well?**

....

Human Organ System

Q1 | Write the names of the nine major organ systems of the Human Body.

1) ....

2) ....

3) ....

4) ....

5) ....

6) ....

7) ....

8) ....

9) ....

Q2 | Label the diagram below with the names of the five sense organs.

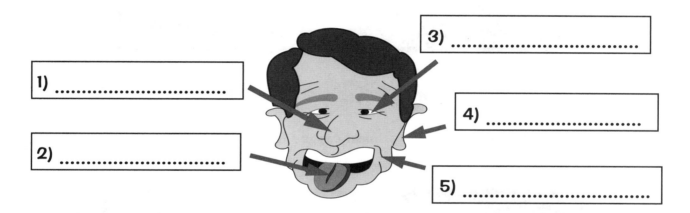

1) ....

2) ....

3) ....

4) ....

5) ....

Q3 | Which organ system is responsible for taking in oxygen and removing carbon dioxide?

....

Q4 | The skeleton has two main jobs.

a) | Name the two main jobs of the skeleton.

1) ....

2) ....

b) | What important job does the skull have to perform every time you bang your head?

....

....

Nutrition

Q1 Name the seven food groups which are essential for healthy living.

1) Carbohydrates
2) Proteins
3) Fats
4) Vitamins
5) Minerals
6) Roughage
7) Water

Q2 Which of the following food groups is the best source of protein? Circle the correct food group.

bread / potatoes / cereals   meat / eggs / fish   butter / cooking oil / cream

Q3 Blood, teeth, nerves and the thyroid gland are kept healthy by taking the right amount of which food group?

Minerals

Q4 Why are carbohydrates important for the body?

Carbohydrates are like fuel for the body. When you are growing up or exercing you need this. (It gives you energy)

Q5 Why is it important to drink lots of water?

Your body is made up of a lot of things but most of it is water. (75% of it is). All chemical reactions take place in water. (eg: Digestion) Its very important!

money, braces, gum

Digestion

Q1 | **What is meant by the word "digestion"?**

Digestion is all breaking down food. There are two steps to it: you firstly break down the food with your teeth. Then when you've swallowed the food your body does the work with agents called enzymes.

Q2 | **What are the two main steps in the process of digestion?**

1) ....

2) ...... Answer ....

Q3 | **In the diagram below, label the six main parts of the digestive system.**

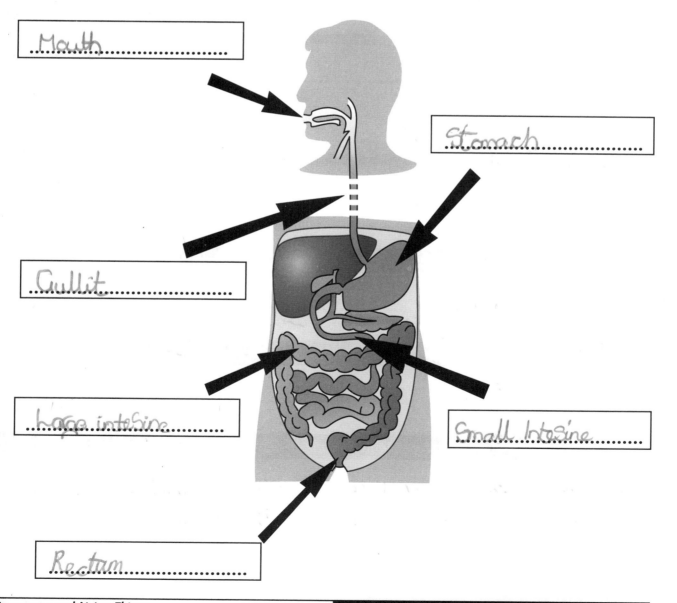

Mouth

Stomach

Gullit

Large intestine

Small Intesine

Rectum

Absorption in the Gut

Q1 | Complete the following sentences about absorption by circling the correct words.

Enzymes are used to _break up_ / _combine_ big molecules so that small ones can be made. These smaller molecules _cannot_ / _can_ pass through the gut wall into the blood. They then pass _into_ / _out of_ the cells and are used by the body.

Q2 | On the diagram below, label the names of the three different types of enzyme the body uses to help it absorb food.

Starch → Carbohydrates → **Glucose and other simple sugars**

Protein → Protease ? → **Amino acids**

Had to look on the page for these too

Fats → Lipase ? → **Glycerol Fatty Acids**

Q3 | In which part of the digestive system is food absorbed?

Small intestine

Q4 | In which part of the digestive system is water absorbed?

Large intestine

Q5 | The small intestine is covered with millions of villi. What are villi and what is their job?

I needed help.

They are finger like projections and villis are good for absorbing food in to the blood.

Taken out
of the curriculum
but still important

The Circulatory System

9

Q1 Complete the sentences below about the circulatory system. Fill in the gaps correctly using the words from the grey box.

oxygen	4	oxygenated	deoxygenated	heart	
	pumped	2	3	oxygen	1

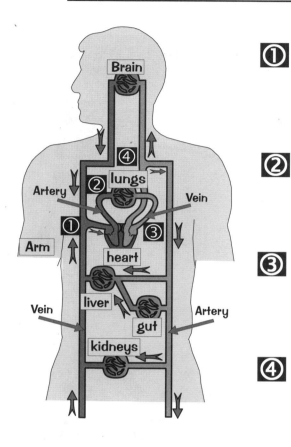

① ....
blood enters the heart

② It's then pumped to the lungs to pick up some ....

③ It's now ....
and travels back to the ....

④ It's then .... around the body so every cell gets the vital .... that it needs.

The sequence then *repeats*

from step number ......

Q2 Label the following blood vessels correctly using the following words: Arteries, capillaries, veins.

Valves keep flow in right direction

These have thin walls which help food particles etc. to pass through.

These carry blood at low pressure back to the heart.

These carry blood at high pressure away from the heart.

....

Skeleton, Joints and Muscles

Q1 **What are the three key functions of the human skeleton?**

1) Movement ....

2) Support ....

3) Protection ....

Q2 **Look at the diagram of the Human Skeleton.**

a) **What is the job of the backbone?**

It can move it a bit....
And it keeps you up
So you don't fall and flop over.

b) **What is the job of the rib cage?**

The job for the rib cage is
to protect small and big
organs. eg: Heart

Backbone

Rib

Q3 **Draw arrows to match up these examples of bones to the correct descriptions.**

knee

skull

spine

| immovable | slightly movable | freely movable |

Q4 **Complete the following sentences about muscles by circling the correct words.**

Muscles work in *pairs* / *trios* against each other. One muscle contracts while the other *two* / *one* relaxes (lengthens), and vice versa. *Tendons* / *ligaments* attach the muscles to the bones. One *muscle* / *cockle* pulls the bone in one direction and the other pulls it in the *opposite* / *same* direction.

Growing Up

Q1 **Label the following diagram of the Human male reproductive system.**

Tube from the ....

....

....

....

....

Q2 **Label the following diagram of the Human female reproductive system.**

....

....

....

....

....

Q3 **The female menstrual cycle is a 28 day cycle. Read the descriptions below and write down whether they occur on the 1st, 4th, 14th or 28th day of the cycle.**

Day Number

The *lining* of the uterus starts to build up again. ....

The wall remains thick awaiting the arrival of a fertilised egg. ....

An egg is released from the ovaries of the female. ....

Bleeding starts as the lining of the uterus (the womb) breaks down and passes out of the vagina. ....

If you're stuck... see Pages 12/13 of our KS3 Revision Guide (Levels 3-6) ☺

Having a Baby

Q1 **Fill in the missing labels.**

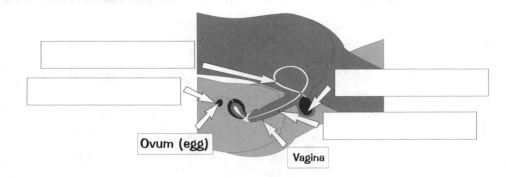

Ovum (egg)

Vagina

Q2 **Put the following stages of fertilisation in the correct order.**

cell division, ovulation, implantation, fertilisation, copulation

1 ....

2 ....

3 ....

4 ....

5 ....

Q3 **Complete the following diagram using the words provided.**

Embryo

Mother's blood

Umbilical cord

Placenta

Amnion (bag)

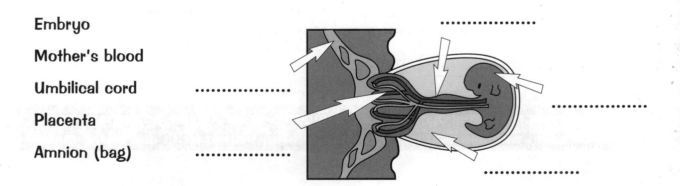

Q4 **At what time after conception do the following developments occur?**

.... month(s)   .... month(s)   .... month(s)   .... month(s)

The embryo has a brain, heart, eyes and legs.

It kicks and it's pesky finger nails can be felt.

The foetus is viable.

The baby is fully developed

Breathing

Q1 Label the diagram below using words from the list on the right.

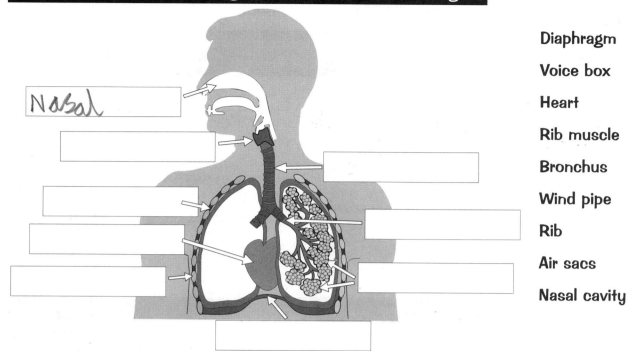

Nasal

Diaphragm

Voice box

Heart

Rib muscle

Bronchus

Wind pipe

Rib

Air sacs

Nasal cavity

Q2 Use the following words to fill in the spaces:

blood,   lungs,   breathing,   oxygen,   air,   carbon dioxide,   energy.

The _____ we need to stay alive comes from the _____

which enters our _____.

The waste gases, _____ _____ and water vapour

leave our body and the whole process is called _____.

The important gas we take in is absorbed into our _____ and

is used with sugar in the cells to give us _____.

Q3 Describe the process of a) breathing in, and b) breathing out.
Use the diagrams to help you.

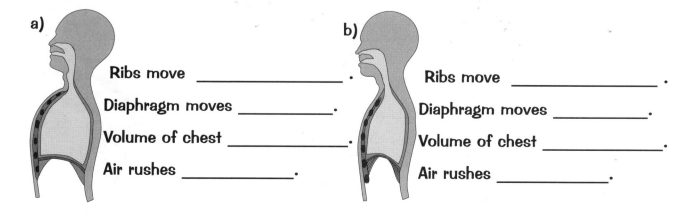

a)

Ribs move _____ .

Diaphragm moves _____ .

Volume of chest _____ .

Air rushes _____ .

b)

Ribs move _____ .

Diaphragm moves _____ .

Volume of chest _____ .

Air rushes _____ .

Smoking

Q1 The apparatus below has been set up to represent what happens to a person's lungs when they smoke a cigarette.

Explain what will happen to a) the temperature and b) the glass wool when the cigarette smoke is sucked through the glass tubing.

....

....

....

....

....

Thermometer

To vacuum pump

Cigarette

Glass 'U' tube

Nice white glass wool

Q2 **Complete the table below showing the three types of grot smoking puts in our lungs.**

Type of Grot	What the Grot does to the body
....	Is an addictive drug that raises the heart beat rate, narrows the arteries and causes high blood pressure. This leads to <u>HEART DISEASE.</u>
Tar	....
....	This is a <u>poisonous gas</u> which joins up with red blood cells making them incapable of transporting OXYGEN around the body.

Q3 **List five of the bad effects that smoking has on your body.**

1 ....

2 ....

3 ....

4 ....

5 ....

Respiration

Q1 Complete the word equation for respiration.
The first letter of each word has already been put in.

G........ + O........ = C........ d........ + W...... | + E........

Q2 The experiment below shows a girl blowing into a tube. The tube goes through a trough of iced water and then into a beaker containing limewater.

After breathing into the tube, water residue was found in the U-tube and the limewater had gone cloudy.

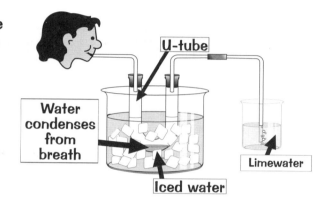

U-tube

Water condenses from breath

Limewater

Iced water

Explain why:
a) there was water residue in the U-tube
b) the limewater was cloudy.

a) ....

....

b) ....

....

Q3 The energy created from respiration is used by the body in many ways.
Use the graphics beneath to help you remember six of them.

1 ....

2 ....

3 ....

4 ....

5 ....

6 ....

Don't worry about this guy, he's just a red herring.

If you're stuck... see Page 17 of our KS3 Revision Guide (Levels 3-6) ☺

Health

Q1 **Having a healthy body means several things. Fill in the blanks in the list below.**

a) The absence of ....

b) Eating a balanced ....

c) Doing enough ....

d) Not abusing ....

Q2 **Complete the following paragraph adding words from the word lists given.**

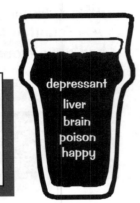

Alcohol is a ...., despite the fact that it may give a .... feeling.
It's a .... which affects the .... and .... leading to various health problems.

depressant
liver
brain
poison
happy

lungs, character, brain, liver, mind, kidneys, behaviour

Solvents are drugs because they cause hallucinations, which are illusions of the .... Solvents can have psychological effects on the .... and .... of the abuser.
They also cause serious damage to the ...., the ...., ... and ....

Q3 **Match the illegal drug to the effects they cause.**

| Hallucinogens |
| Pain Killers |
| Stimulants |
| Depressants |

Examples: Heroin and Morphine. They are extremely addictive and can both cause severe degeneration of a person's life.

Examples: Ecstasy and LSD. Ecstasy can give the feeling of boundless energy which can lead to overheating, dehydration and sometimes DEATH.

Example: Barbiturates. They slow down a persons body which can be dangerous. They can help sleeping but they're seriously habit-forming.

Examples: Amphetamine (speed) and Methedrine. They give a feeling of boundless energy, they're addictive so behaviour and personality change.

Fighting Disease

Q1 Fill in the gaps. All the words you need are in the grey box.

> immune, medicines, white, blood, cells, natural,
> immunisation, antibodies, defences

The body has its own .... against

disease but it can be helped by .... and

.... The main armies of defence of the body are

.... and ....

.... which are part of the body's .... system.

Q2 Do antibiotics work on bacteria, viruses or both? ....

Q3 Give two examples of bacterial diseases and two examples of viral diseases.

Bacteria ....  Viruses ....

....

Q4 Find and circle the nine underlined words from the text.

"White blood cells attack microbes in three ways. Firstly they gobble them up whole. Secondly they produce antibodies to neutralise and prepare microbes for gobbling. Lastly they neutralise any poisons or toxins produced by the microbes. Once the white blood cells recognise a microbe they can act immediately to stop you getting ill. This is called immunity"

M	G	N	I	K	O	M	S	E	V	I	E	W
D	I	I	J	B	C	I	L	I	A	T	S	H
E	B	C	E	L	L	S	E	Z	N	B	I	I
C	S	R	R	O	N	M	O	N	O	X	L	T
S	E	I	D	O	B	I	T	N	A	S	A	E
M	S	W	L	D	B	P	I	P	N	G	R	P
Q	I	J	D	A	C	E	A	O	Q	O	T	L
S	L	R	O	N	C	H	S	O	L	E	U	U
N	Y	P	E	T	T	I	I	N	H	A	E	O
I	J	V	R	U	O	M	U	T	E	G	N	D
X	N	J	D	P	B	L	A	R	I	O	E	C
O	M	R	F	Y	T	I	N	U	M	M	I	C
T	M	R	F	W	T	M	U	C	U	S	C	C

How Plants Make Food

Q1 What do plants use photosynthesis to make? ....

Q2 Use the words from the word list to complete the photosynthesis equation.

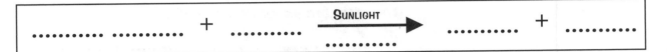

Oxygen, Water, Glucose, Carbon dioxide, Chlorophyll

.... + ... $\xrightarrow[\text{.............}]{\text{SUNLIGHT}}$ .... + ...

Q3 Fill in the blanks. Each word is something plants need for photosynthesis.

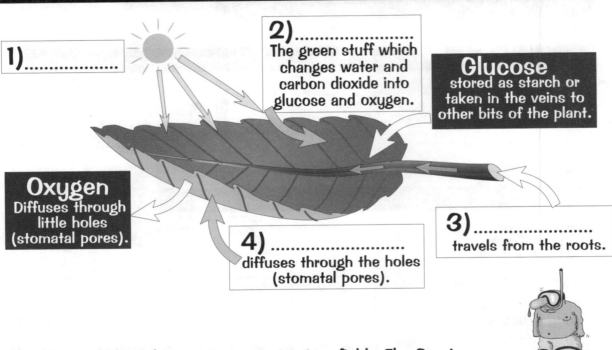

1) ....

2) ....
The green stuff which changes water and carbon dioxide into glucose and oxygen.

Glucose
stored as starch or taken in the veins to other bits of the plant.

Oxygen
Diffuses through little holes (stomatal pores).

4) ....
diffuses through the holes (stomatal pores).

3) ....
travels from the roots.

Q4 The picture below shows a tree growing in a field. The Sun is shining, so photosynthesis is taking place rapidly in the leaves.

a) What substance is _taken in_ from the air by the tree? ....

b) What substance is _given out_ into the air by the tree? ....

c) What substance needed for photosynthesis does the tree take from the soil?

....

Photosynthesis

Q1 Iodine can be used to test for starch in leaves. When tested, the leaves from a plant that had been kept in the dark for 24 hours went brown. The leaves from a plant that had been kept in the light for 24 hours went black.

| Why had starch been produced in the second plant and not the first? |

....

Q2 | Complete this crossword about photosynthesis.

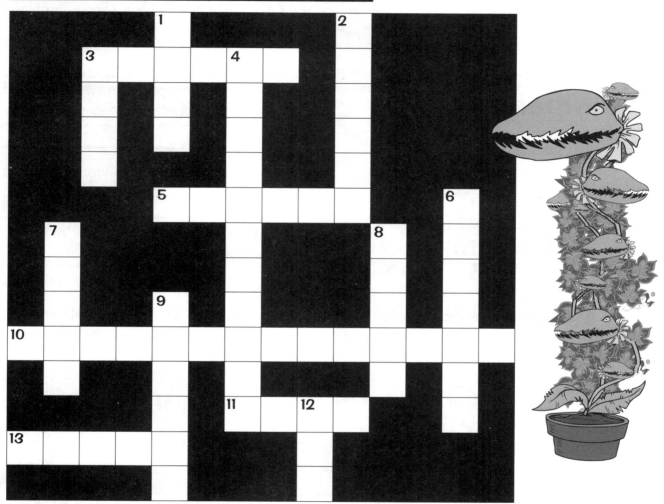

Across

3) Sugars are stored as this (6).

5) across and **6)** down — gas needed for photosynthesis (6,7)

10) How plants make food (14)

11) Food is made here (4)

13) Chlorophyll looks like this (5)

Down

1) Plants can't photosynthesise in this (4)

2) We need it — plants make it in the light (6)

3) Roots get water from here (4)

4) Pigment that absorbs light (11)

6) see 5) across

7) Energy needed to make sugars (5)

8) Liquid needed for photosynthesis (5)

9) Test for starch with this solution (6)

12) Carbon dioxide comes from here (3)

Plant Growth

Q1 Give two special features that make root hairs good at absorption.

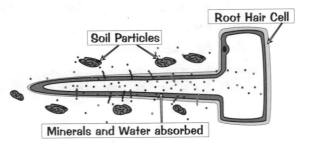

1 ....

2 ....

Q2 Nitrates, phosphates and potassium are the three essential minerals needed by plants.

Match up the essential minerals with what they do.

| Nitrates | | Provide phosphorous which is needed for photosynthesis and respiration. |

| Phosphates | | Helps enzymes to work properly. |

| Potassium | | Provide nitrogen which is needed for making proteins. |

Q3 Plants show specific symptoms if they are missing one of the essential minerals.

Complete the sentences below that say what each plant is missing.

 A _small_ plant with _yellow_ older leaves.  This plant is lacking ....

 _Poor root growth_ and _purple_ younger leaves.  This plant is lacking ....

 _Yellow_ leaves with _dead bits_.  This plant is lacking ....

Plant Reproduction

Q1 Use the words from the word list to label the parts of the flower shown below.

anther, filament, petals, stigma, style, ovary, sepals

1) Stamens

....

....

2) Carpel

....

....

....

3) ....

4) ....

Q2 What are the male parts of the flower called? ....

Q3 What are the female parts of the flower called? ....

Q4 Complete the sentences by joining a beginning with an ending with an arrow:

Beginnings

Endings

the female sex cell in plants is called

the female sex organ in plants is called

the female sex organ is made up from

the male sex cell in plants is called

the male sex organ in plants is called

the male sex organ is made up from

the filament and anther

the stigma, style and ovary

the carpel

the stamen

the pollen

the ova

Q5 Write down the differences between these two flowers and say whether they are wind or insect pollinated.

....

....

....

....

....

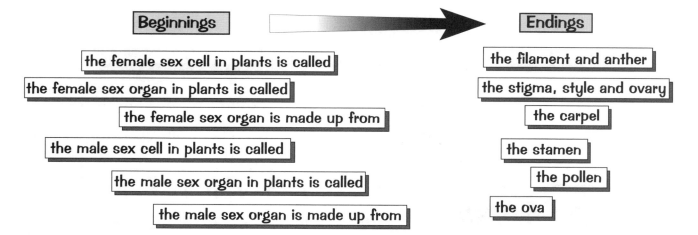

A   B

If you're stuck... see Page 24 of our KS3 Revision Guide (Levels 3-6) ☺

Taken out
of the curriculum
but still important

Plant Reproduction and Seeds

Q1 Plants disperse their seeds in a number of ways.

Write down whether the following are dispersed by the wind, animals or explosively.

**Burdock fruit
(has tiny hooks)**

Sycamore fruit

Tomato fruit

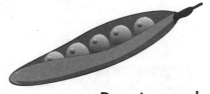

Peas in a pod

Dandelion fruit

Wind dispersed: ....

Dispersed by animals: ....

Dispersed by explosion: ....

Q2 Germination is when the seeds start to grow.

What three conditions need to be just right for germination to happen?

....

....

Q3

Have a go at the flower wordsearch.

The words to find are:

anther, filament, ovary, ovule, pollen, stigma, style.

There are two other words in the grid to do with flowers — can you find them both?

Here's a clue..

S _ _ _ _ _ N
C _ _ _ _ _ L

woah, look
at all the
letters dude

W	P	A	O	V	U	L	E	R	A
C	Z	N	T	E	B	Z	E	M	O
A	E	T	N	I	H	E	G	V	G
R	Y	H	E	U	U	I	I	D	S
P	R	E	M	Z	T	K	E	X	P
E	A	R	A	S	Q	X	A	S	O
L	V	F	L	D	F	N	T	S	L
N	O	K	I	C	O	Y	O	L	L
H	P	A	F	Q	L	D	N	P	E
S	T	A	M	E	N	Y	Y	B	N

The Carbon Cycle

Q1 Carbon is an important element because it is found in all living things. It's constantly recycled through the environment in the carbon cycle. The scene below shows some important steps in this cycle.

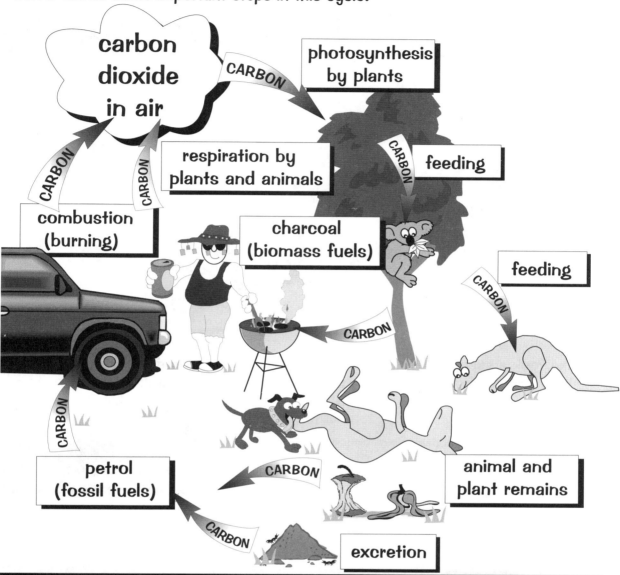

a) Which two processes in the picture contribute to the carbon dioxide in the air?

....

b) Plants take in carbon dioxide through photosynthesis. How does the carbon then get into animals?

....

c) Where does the carbon found in fossil fuels come from?

....

....

Inherited and Environmental Variation

Q1 Animals and plants do not all look the same, they vary. Some of this variation is inherited from their parents, and some is caused by the environment (where a plant grows, how you are brought up and what you eat, for example).

> Look at the picture of Jane below and put a tick next to each of her characteristics which have been inherited from her parents.

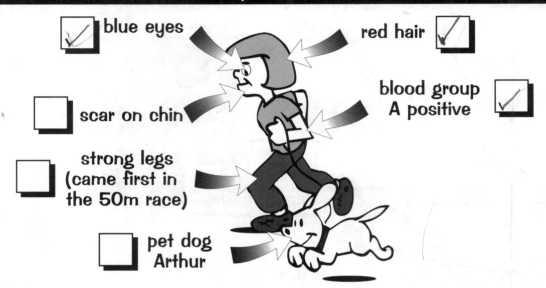

blue eyes ☑

red hair ☑

blood group A positive ☑

scar on chin ☐

strong legs (came first in the 50m race) ☐

pet dog Arthur ☐

Q2 Mike took a seed from his dad's enormous sunflower plant in the greenhouse. He planted it in a pot in the garden expecting it to grow as big as him but after a month it was only half his size.

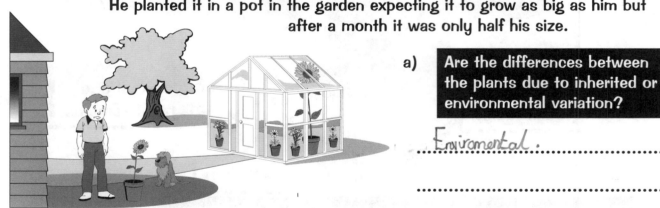

a) **Are the differences between the plants due to inherited or environmental variation?**

Enviromental.

b) **What are the four factors which might have affected his plant's growth?**

Light , Water , Temprature and Soil.

c) **What could Mike do to make his plant grow better?**

Ask his dad what he did to the Sunflower to get it so big.

Classification

Q1 Look at the animals below and put a tick next to all of the vertebrates (those with a backbone) and a cross next to the invertebrates (those without a backbone).

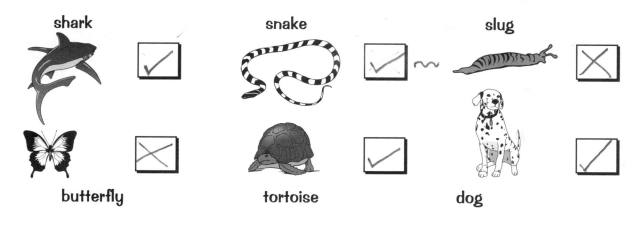

shark ✓   snake ✓   slug ✗

butterfly ✗   tortoise ✓   dog ✓

Q2 Sarah saw some creatures in and around the pond in her garden. Classify each one as either insect, fish, amphibian or mollusc.

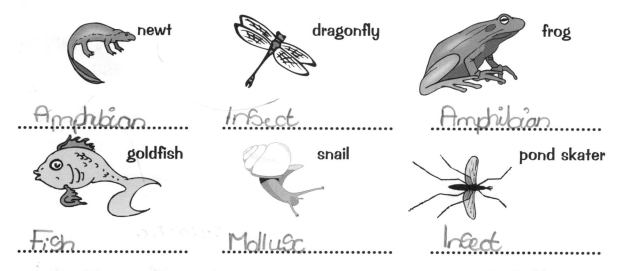

newt ...... Amphibian ......   dragonfly ...... Insect ......   frog ...... Amphibian ......

goldfish ...... Fish ......   snail ...... Mollusc ......   pond skater ...... Insect ......

Q3 Choose words from below to fill in the sentences about birds and mammals.

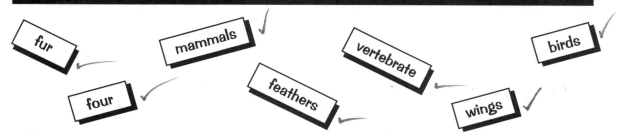

fur ✓   mammals ✓   vertebrate ✓   birds ✓   four ✓   feathers ✓   wings ✓

Birds and mammals have backbones and so belong to the _vertebrate_ group of animals.

Birds have _feathers_ , _wings_ and a beak while mammals have _fur_

or hair and _four_ limbs.

mammals give birth to live young unlike _birds_ which lay eggs.

If you're stuck... see Page 30 of our KS3 Revision Guide (Levels 3-6) ☺

Taken out
of the curriculum
but still important

Using Keys

Q1 Four aliens were found in a crater on the Moon. Use the key from the alien identification manual to classify them and write their names in the spaces.

A	B	C	D

...Grabbing... ...Standard... ...Armless... ...Easy...
...Flappoid... ...Moonoid... ...Flappoid... ...Moonoid...

1) Does the alien have flight appendages (wings)?

YES .... go to question 2)

NO .... go to question 3)

2) Does it have arms for grabbing scared astronauts?

YES .... alien is a **GRABBING FLAPPOID**

NO .... alien is an **ARMLESS FLAPPOID**

3) Does it have antennae for picking up radio signals from Earth?

YES .... alien is an **EASY LISTENOID**

NO .... alien is a **STANDARD MOONOID**

Q2 Use the key below to identify these four prehistoric characters.

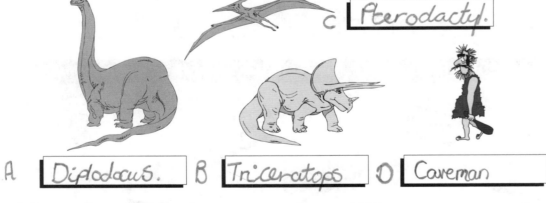

C Pterodactyl.

A Diplodocus.   B Triceratops   D Caveman

1) Does it have four legs?   YES .... go to question 2

NO .... go to question 3

2) Does it have pointy bits on its head?   YES .... it is a **TRICERATOPS**

NO .... it is a **DIPLODOCUS**

3) Does it have a club and say 'ugh' a lot?   YES .... it is a **CAVEMAN**

NO .... it is a **PTERODACTYL**

Adaptation

Q1 Polar bears are adapted to live in a very cold habitat. Fill in the blanks in the paragraph below with these words:

arctic   heat loss

fat

warm   rounded

Polar bears have special features to help them live in __arctic__

conditions. They have a thick layer of __fat__ and a thick fur

coat to keep them __warm__. Their __rounded__ shape

gives them a small surface area to reduce __heat loss__.

Q2 Complete the sentences about the adaptations the camel has for living in the desert using the words below.

feet   store   drink   sand   fat   hump

Camels can _____ and _____ lots of water which is handy for those long dry spells.

_____ is stored in its _____ to assist the loss of heat from the rest of its body.

Big, wide _____ stop it from sinking in the soft _____.

Food Chains

Q1 Here is a food chain you might find in your own garden.

Leaf → Worm → Bird → Cat

a) What do the arrows mean in food chains?

....

b) Name an animal from the food chain which is a herbivore.

....

c) Which animal is a carnivore?

....

Q2 Draw lines to connect the words on the left with their correct meanings.

carnivores

omnivores

herbivores

consumers

producers

animals that can eat both plants and animals

animals that eat plants

animals that eat other animals

organisms that can make their own food

organisms that rely on other organisms for their food

Q3 The names below are all words to do with food chains, but with the letters muddled up. Unscramble the letters to find out what the words are and then find them in the word search. The first one has been done for you:

Vince Roar, Mrs Oncue, Dina Choof,   Ron Movie, Dr Prouce, Rover Hibe.

carnivore ....

....

....

....

....

....

E	P	C	O	N	S	U	M	E	R
R	R	F	O	I	D	C	H	A	O
O	E	O	O	A	E	R	B	M	I
V	C	O	M	H	I	V	N	C	A
I	U	D	A	C	H	I	N	G	R
B	D	C	E	D	V	O	R	E	S
R	O	H	S	O	K	I	Z	X	L
E	R	A	R	O	A	R	N	I	V
H	P	E	R	F	V	I	B	R	A
X	E	R	O	V	I	N	R	A	C

Food Webs

Q1 Below is a food web found in rivers and waterways.

a) Fill in the letters missing in each word.

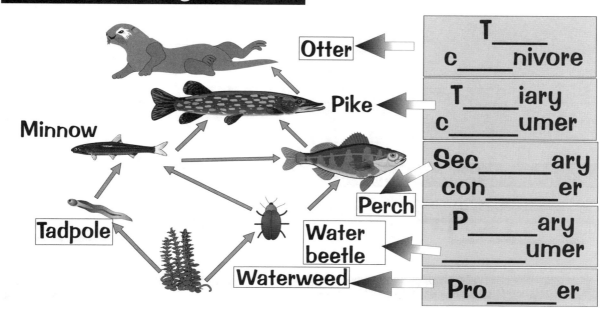

Otter

Pike

Minnow

Perch

Tadpole

Water beetle

Waterweed

T____
c____nivore

T____iary
c____umer

Sec_____ary
con_____er

P_____ary
_____umer

Pro_____er

b) Which of these animals are herbivores?

....

....

c) Which of these animals are carnivores?

....

....

....

....

d) What do minnows eat?

....

....

e) A fisherman came and caught all of the perch. Circle the correct answer in these questions about what will happen in the foodweb.

There will be   _more_ / _less_   water beetles so the water weed will be eaten   _more_ / _less_.

The minnows will have   _more_ / _less_   food but will be eaten   _more_ / _less_   by the pike.

Problems in Food Chains

Q1 Look at the pyramid of numbers below and answer the following questions.

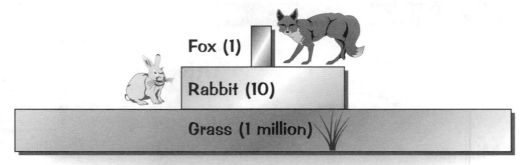

Fox (1)

Rabbit (10)

Grass (1 million)

a) Complete this food chain with the organisms from above.

[   ] ⟹ [   ] ⟹ [   ]

b) What information does the pyramid give us about each level in the food chain?

....

....

....

c) The grass is growing in a field which has been sprayed with pesticide. What will happen to the level of pesticide as it is passed along the food chain?

....

....

Q2 Draw a pyramid of numbers for the food chain below and next to it draw an arrow showing the direction in which energy is passed.

oak tree (1) → caterpillar (100) → blue tit (10)

energy is passed
this way

Survival

Q1   Look at these three lobsters and answer the questions below:

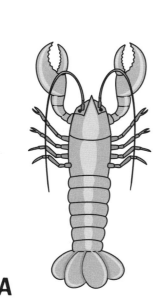

A   **B**   **C**

a)   What adaptation do lobsters use to catch their prey and protect themselves?

....

b)   In a population of lobsters which lobster would be most likely to survive? Why?

....

....

....

c)   Use these words to finish the paragraph below.

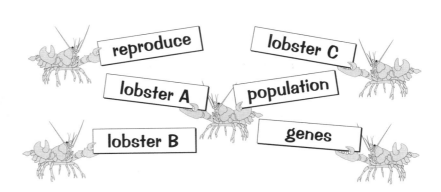

reproduce   lobster C   lobster A   population   lobster B   genes

In a population of lobsters the individuals which are most like _____

would survive best. This means that they are more likely to _____

and pass their _____ on to their young. Gradually the whole

population would become more and more like _____ .

If you're stuck... see Page 38 of our KS3 Revision Guide (Levels 3-6) ☺

Mon. 27/9

Types of Material

Q1   Five different materials are listed below. Under each material is an example of one of its uses.

Explain why that material is well suited to its use.

a) Metal (making car, van bodies etc.)

Metal are strong and can carry wieght but also can be sqashed if is cashed.

b) Plastic (plugs and wire insulation)

It flexible, easy shaped, good inslators of electricity and some are acid resistant. S

c) Glass (lightbulbs)

They are transparent or translucent so it can let light out and is hard but brittle.

d) Fibres (clothes)

Fibres can be natural or synthetic. And some maybe strong and most are bendy so can sit on you easly. (cloths)

e) Ceramics (bricks)

Their very strong if compressed and hard and brittle.

Q2   **Some of the above materials are recyclable. What does this mean?**

That Recylable means after using them don't through them away either refuse them or send them away to be made into something else.

Q3   **Reinforced concrete is made out of concrete with steel bars running through it.**

Why do you think this gives it so much strength?

Because steel is metal and metals are strong and concrete is ceramics and ceramics are very strong if compressed.

Materials and their Properties

Q1 A list of words describing the various properties of some materials is given below.

List three useful properties of the material used to make the window pane and the girder. Some properties are given below to help you.

conductor of electricity   magnetic

flexible   hard   malleable   brittle   insulator of electricity

strong   transparent   insulator of heat

conductor of heat   translucent

window pane

a *Transparent*

b *Hard*

c *But brittle*

steel girder

d *Strong (very)*

e *Magnetic*

f *Conductor of heat + electricity.*

Q2 Why is rubber used for tyres? Use some of the words above to help you answer.

It is used because it is... *Strong, flexible and can be melted to fit the tyre shape.*

Q3 Why do most metal saucepans have non-metal handles?

Pan Handle

Non-metals are... *Conductors of heat So if you have a metal handle to you will burn your self.*

Q4 Match the following materials (on the left) to the word which best describes them.

toffee bar

electrical plug casing

compass needle

horse shoe

diamond

malleable when heated

hard

tasty

insulator

magnetic

Solids, Liquids and Gases

Q1 Complete the table by writing in whether you think the substance is solid, liquid or gas.

Substance	Solid, Liquid or Gas
Cheese	
Treacle	
Steam	
Jelly	
Glass	
Petrol	
Paper	
Dry Air	

Q2 Complete the crossword by answering the clues and filling in the boxes.

Clues:

Down

1. One way of making a gas occupy a smaller volume is by .... it. (11)
4. Another way of saying how much 'space' a substance takes up. (6)

Across

2. Hardness is a useful .... of diamond (8)
3. The number of states of matter (5)
5. The hardest state of matter to squash (5)
6. This state of matter always matches the shape of its container (6)
7. The least dense of all the states of matter (3)

Solids, Liquids and Gases

Q3 **For each of the diagrams below, write down whether it is solid, liquid or gas.**

A

B

C

answer

answer

answer

Q4 **Ice floats in water. What does this tell you about the density of ice compared to that of water? Why is this unusual?**

....

....

....

Q5 **Complete the following sentences using the words given in the cloud.**

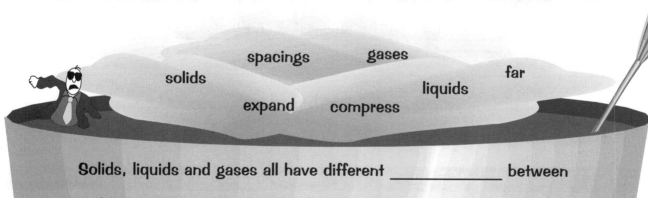

spacings   gases   solids   far   liquids   expand   compress

Solids, liquids and gases all have different _____ between

their particles. The particles in a gas are quite _____

apart compared to the particles in liquids and solids. Because of

this, it is very easy to _____ a gas but not so easy to do

the same to a liquid or solid. _____ will take the shape of

any container they are put in, whereas _____ keep their

shape. Finally, _____ will _____ to fill any

available space in a container.

If you're stuck... see Page 42 of our KS3 Revision Guide (Levels 3-6) ☺

Physical Changes

Q1 Look at the diagram below. What are the names given to the different changes of state? One has been done for you.

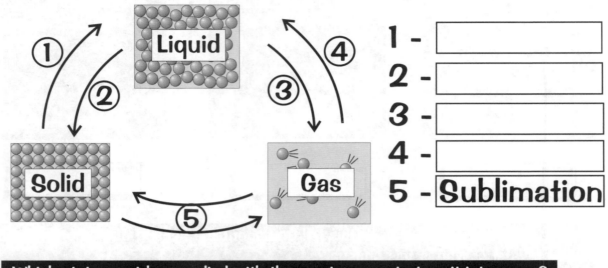

1 -
2 -
3 -
4 -
5 - **Sublimation**

Q2 Which state must be supplied with the most energy to turn it into a gas? Explain your answer.

....

....

Q3 When energy is supplied to a solid, what happens to the particles within it? Answer in terms of the energies of the particles and the distances between them.

....

....

....

Q4 What is diffusion? Explain how a nasty smell might spread across your classroom.

....

....

....

....

....

....

....

Physical Changes

Taken out
of the curriculum
but still important

Q5 Fill in the blanks in the heating curve using the words given in the word box.

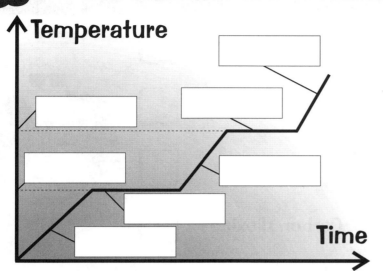

Temperature

Time

word list

boiling point

melting point

solid

melting

liquid

boiling

gas

Q6 Match the correct word to its description. The first has been done for you.

The name given to the solid being dissolved — solution

The liquid that the solid is being dissolved into — saturated

The name given to the mixture of the dissolving solid and liquid — solubility

If the solid will dissolve, it is known as... — solute

But if the solid won't dissolve, it is known as... — solvent

If the liquid won't allow you to dissolve any more solid in it, it is... — soluble

The amount of solid a liquid will allow to dissolve in it — insoluble

wot you looking at?

Q7 Draw a labelled diagram in the box below to show how you would measure the freezing point of water. You should use a thermometer, filter funnel, conical flask/beaker and ice.

Atoms and Elements

Q1 Which of the following are elements, which are compounds and which are neither? Put an **E**, a **C** or an **N** in the box next to the substance.

Carbon ☐   My pet hamster ☐

Air ☐   Uranium ☐

All Saints ☐   Helium ☐

Nitrogen ☐   Carbon dioxide ☐

Q2 The Periodic Table contains all the elements.
What is a group and a period in the Periodic Table?

....

....

....

Q3 Fill in the blanks in the following passage using the words provided.

Elements consist of one type of _____. Elements can't be split up into anything simpler by _____ methods. There are about _____ different elements. Each one has a name and a shorthand _____, e.g. Carbon, C. Everything on Earth is made up of _____. The Periodic Table is made up of groups and periods. Some groups have names, such as group 1, the _____ metals, group 7, the _____ and group 0, the _____ gases.

chemical

atom

100

halogens

elements

alkali

symbol

noble

Q4 Of the three diagrams below, which is a pure element? Tick the box.

☐   ☐   ☐

Compounds

Q1 What is the difference between an element and a compound?

....

....

....

Q2 Divide the following into two sets, _elements_ and _compounds_, by writing them on the correct lines below.

Sulphur   Magnesium Oxide   Water

Lead   Carbon Dioxide

Sodium Chloride

Oxygen   Sulphuric Acid

Helium   Calcium

Sulphur Dioxide   Carbon Monoxide   Chlorine

Elements:

....

....

Compounds:

....

....

Q3 What elements do the following compounds contain?

carbon dioxide ....

copper sulphate ....

Q4 Name a compound that contains the following elements...

iron, sulphur and oxygen ....

hydrogen and sulphur ....

40

Properties of Metals

Q1 Shade in the part of the Periodic Table (below) that corresponds to *metals*.

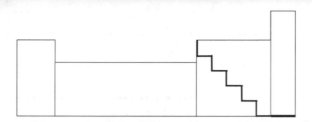

Q2 Describe some of the main differences between metals and non-metals. Use the following words and phrases in your answer.

> melting point   densities   boiling point
> Periodic Table   good conductors of heat & electricity
> bad conductors of heat & electricity

....

....

....

Q3 Some pretty pictures describing the marvellous properties of metals are shown below. Under each picture write down what property is being demonstrated.

....

Q4 Match the following metals up to their common uses (think about why you would choose that use for the metal).

1. Copper	A. Used for rust prevention
2. Lead	B. Used for bridges
3. Aluminium	C. Used for wiring
4. Gold	D. Used to keep out radiation
5. Bronze	E. Used in thermometers
6. Steel	F. Used for making statues
7. Zinc	G. Used for jewellery
8. Mercury	H. Used for aircraft

Properties of Non-metals

Q1 What state are most non-metals in at room temperature? What does this tell you about the particles in non-metals? (hint — think about the 'Physical Changes' section)

....

....

....

Q2 A few diagrams of non-metals are given below. What properties of non-metals do you think they are describing? Write your answers in the boxes.

You can't travel on this bus pal!

Well I'm going to find a decent conductor   Heat

The Non Metal Bus

This carbon brush keeps wearing out

no. 1 Fatboy weightwatcher   z z z

Q3 Look at the table below, then complete parts a) - d):

Element	Symbol	Melting Point (°C)	Boiling Point (°C)	State at 20°C
Sulphur		112	444	
Oxygen		-218	-183	
Bromine		-7	58	
Neon		-248	-246	
Iodine		114	183	

on to the next section!!!

a) Write in the symbol of each element.

b) Write in the state of each element at room temperature (20°C).

c) Tick the non-metal which is a liquid at room temperature.

d) In which state would you find the majority of non-metals at room temperature?

....

Mixtures

Q1 **Tick the explanation which best describes a mixture.**

- ○ A single substance.
- ○ A number of substances.
- ○ Several substances combined. Separable by physical means.
- ○ Several elements combined. Only separable by chemical means.

Q2 Four important ways of separating things are listed below.

Join up the parts of the words to show them.

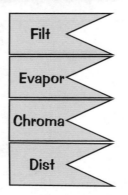

Filt	tography
Evapor	ration
Chroma	illation
Dist	ation

Q3 Byron was told that ink is a mixture of dye and water. He decided to test this theory by using the apparatus shown.

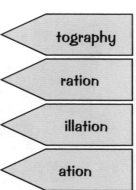

ink

heat

test tube

iced water

water

After heating for a while he found that a clear liquid was formed in the test tube.

Answer the following questions.

a) **Why was ice used in the beaker?**

....

....

b) **How could Byron show that this clear liquid was water?**

....

....

Mixtures

c) | **Which of these statements is true about this experiment?**

○ The dyes in the ink boil off, cool and are collected.

○ The ink boils off, cools and is then collected.

○ The water in the ink boils off, cools and is then collected.

○ The steam pushes the ink out of the flask.

Q4   *Clive, a well known local scientist, discovered a dent in the door of his new red car. He suspected three clumsy neighbours, each of which had red paint on the bumpers of their green cars — one of them must have dented his pride and joy. Tearfully, he removed samples of red paint form each neighbours bumper and examined the colours using chromatography.*

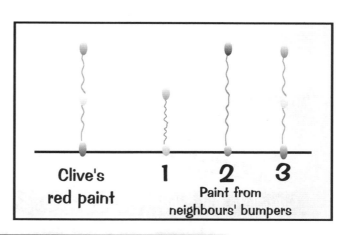

a) | **How many paint pigments are found in the red paint of Clive's car?**

....

....

b) | **What must be used to make the paints split up into the various pigments?**

....

c) | **Explain in detail how chromatography is being used in this investigation.**

....

....

....

d) | **Which neighbour appears to be the clumsy one who bumped Clive's car?**

....

Geological Changes

The rock cycle involves changing the three rock types *(igneous, sedimentary and metamorphic)* from one to another. The picture below illustrates the rock cycle.

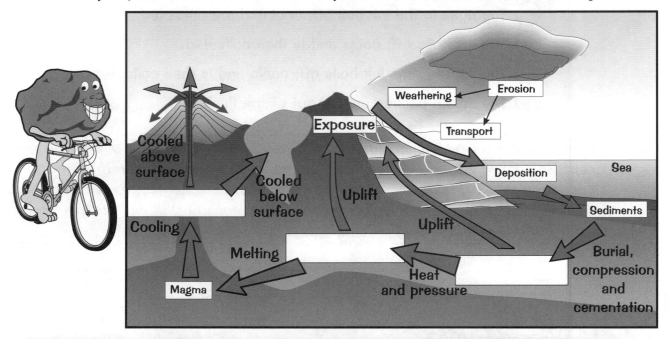

Q1 **Complete the rock cycle picture by putting in the three rock types listed below:**

igneous rocks   sedimentary rocks   metamorphic rocks

Q2 **Complete the following paragraphs by filling in the missing words from the list:**

| igneous | metamorphic | weathering | buried | compressed | heat |
| melt | magma | sea | magma | cools | rock cycle |

Over millions of years rocks change from one type to another. This is called the

_____ _____. *Rocks are broken up by* _____ *and*

washed into the _____ . *Over millions of years these become buried,*

_____ *and cemented and form sedimentary rocks.*

Sometimes these rocks become _____ *deeper into the Earth, and are*

changed by _____ *and pressure into* _____ *rocks.*

If metamorphic rocks are buried still further they can _____ *and become*

_____ . *Pressure forces the* _____ *upwards where it*

_____ *to make* _____ *rocks.*

Geological Changes

Q3 | Complete the sentences about rock types.

let's rock!

Igneous rocks form from ....

....

Sedimentary rocks form from ....

....

Metamorphic rocks form from ....

....

Q4 | Look at the descriptions of various rocks below. Try to identify each type of rock as Igneous, Sedimentary or Metamorphic then tick the correct column in the box below.

Basalt

Chalk

Slate

Grit

Granite

Marble

Obsidian

Sandstone

Marl

Quartzite

A dark rock with small crystals, formed on the surface of the Earth.

A white rock formed from the shells of sea animals which collected at the bottom of shallow seas.

A dark rock showing crystals and layers. It was formed by shale being changed by heat and pressure.

Rock formed from small particles stuck together.

A speckled rock. The speckles are different crystals that have formed from melted rock which cooled slowly inside the earth.

A usually white, hard rock. It is made from crystals, but also shows layers. It is formed from chalk or limestone by heat and pressure.

A glassy rock formed by volcanoes. The melted rock has cooled very quickly, so crystals are unable to form.

A rock formed from small grains of sand which have been squeezed tightly together.

A rock made from small, dark grey fragments which have been squeezed together.

A crystalline rock which has been formed by changes due to heat and pressure within the earth.

Rock	Igneous	Sedimentary	Metamorphic
Basalt			
Chalk			
Slate			
Grit			
Granite			
Marble			
Obsidian			
Sandstone			
Marl			
Quartzite			

If you're stuck... see Page 58/59 of our KS3 Revision Guide (Levels 3-6) ☺

Useful Chemical Change

Q1 **The statements below are about chemical reactions. Tick the circle.**

	True as a true thing	False as a false thing	Don't rightly know
a) Mass isn't lost when the reactants turn into the products.	◯	◯	◯
b) A word equation doesn't show what's going on in a reaction.	◯	◯	◯
c) Chemical reactions involve temporary changes.	◯	◯	◯
d) Reactions always involve a change in energy.	◯	◯	◯
e) Energy is either given out or taken in.	◯	◯	◯
f) The temperature in a reaction will only go up.	◯	◯	◯
g) Visible changes never occur in the reaction mixture.	◯	◯	◯

Q2 **Five very useful, chemical reactions are listed below. For each say why they are so useful.**

a) Combustion is useful because ....

....

b) Fermentation is useful because ....

....

c) Smelting is useful because ....

....

d) Neutralisation is useful because ....

....

e) Electrolysis is useful because ....

....

Q3 Felicity was investigating what makes things rust. She decided to set up the apparatus as shown below.

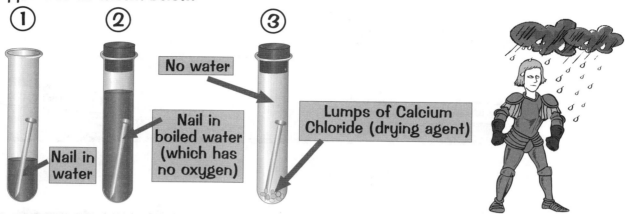

① ② ③

No water

Nail in boiled water (which has no oxygen)

Lumps of Calcium Chloride (drying agent)

Nail in water

a) Complete the table below with the results you would expect her to get.

Tube	Colour of nail before	Colour of nail after
1		
2		
3		

b) In which tube(s) does rusting occur?

....

c) Why is calcium chloride used in this investigation?

....

d) What two things must be in contact with iron for it to rust?

....

Q4 The pictures below show how you can stop rusting. Briefly say how each method stops the reaction of rusting.

OIL IT

PAINT IT

GALVANISE IT

....

....

Reactions of Metals

Q1 Study the information below and then answer the questions.

> iron reacts slowly with water
>
> potassium is hard to remove from its ore
>
> potassium reacts violently with water
>
> copper doesn't react with water
>
> copper is easy to remove from its ore
>
> iron is removed from its ore using carbon

a) **Put the metals in order of reactivity.**

1) ....

2) ....

3) ....

b) **Which metal would you choose to make a water pipe from? Explain your answer.**

Metal ....

Reason ....

....

c) These three metals were then put in three test tubes of hydrochloric acid. The results were mistakenly written on a bit of scrap paper, and so are all jumbled up.

> *Fizzed violently, tube became very hot*
> *Metal sank to bottom, no reaction*
> *Bubbles appeared slowly on the metal*

Sort out the results into the nice table below.

Reaction in acid	Potassium	Copper	Iron
Observations			

Displacement Reactions

Q1 A piece of an unknown metal **X** was placed into a solution of three salts, copper sulphate, magnesium sulphate and iron sulphate. The results of this are shown below.

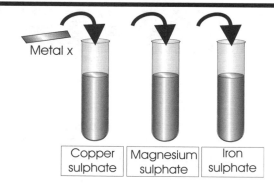

Results

Salt solution	Copper sulphate	Magnesium sulphate	Iron sulphate
Result with X added	Orange solid appeared on metal	No reaction	Grey solid appeared on metal

a) Did a reaction happen between metal **X** and copper sulphate?

....

b) Is metal **X** more or less reactive than copper?

....

c) Did a reaction happen between metal **X** and magnesium sulphate?

....

d) Is metal **X** more or less reactive than magnesium?

....

e) Did a reaction happen between metal **X** and iron sulphate?

....

f) Is metal **X** more or less reactive than iron?

....

g) What is the name given to a reaction where one metal takes the place of another?

....

h) Put copper, magnesium, iron and metal **X** in order of reactivity, *(most reactive to least reactive)*.

....

If you're stuck... see Page 67 of our KS3 Revision Guide (Levels 3-6) ☺

Acids and Alkalis

Q1 Place a tick in the box next to each of the following statements to indicate which is True and which is False.

	True	False
All acids are dangerous		
All alkalis are dangerous		
All acids are dissolved in water		
All alkalis are dissolved in water		
Acids can burn skin		
Alkalis feel soapy		
Lemons contain alkali		
Acids taste sweet		
Acids stop indigestion		
All acids are corrosive		
Acids have a pH above 7		
Acids have a pH below 7		
The pH scale goes from 0 to 14		

Q2 Name three common acids you might find in the lab.

1) ....

2) ....

3) ....

Q3 Name three common alkalis you might find in the lab.

1) ....

2) ....

3) ....

Acids and Alkalis

Q4 | Circle the hazchem symbol that should be used on a bottle of bench acid.

Q5 | Circle the hazchem symbol that should be used on a bottle of bench alkali.

Q6 | List three things you should always do when using acids or alkalis in the laboratory.

1) ....

2) ....

3) ....

Q7 | Tick which of the following contain acids.

○ pickled onions
○ wasp stings
○ car batteries
○ ant stings

Q8 | Which of the following contain alkalis?

○ oven cleaner
○ soaps
○ fertilisers
○ lime

Q9 | Acids react with metals like zinc to make hydrogen gas and react with rocks like limestone to produce carbon dioxide.

What are the tests for hydrogen and carbon dioxide?

....

....

....

   If you're stuck... see Page 71/72 of our KS3 Revision Guide (Levels 3-6) ☺

52

The pH Scale and Indicators

Q1 Litmus is an indicator. In acids it goes red and in alkali it goes blue.

What is an indicator?

....

....

Q2 **Colour in the pH chart below with the correct colours for Universal Indicator solution.**

pH 1 2 3 4 5 6 7 8 9 10 11 12 13 14

_ _ _ ACIDS _ _ _ _ _ _ _ ALKALIS _ _ _

NEUTRAL

Q3 **What values of pH would you expect for:**

a) Lemon juice ....

b) Oven cleaner ....

c) Lime (calcium hydroxide) ....

d) Sodium Chloride (common salt) ....

e) Hydrochloric acid ....

Q4 Look at the following information:

Magnesium oxide pH 10

Ethanoic acid pH 3-4

Potassium chloride pH 7

Potassium hydroxide pH 13

Hydrogen chloride pH 2

Choose an example which is...

a) A strong acid ....

b) A weak acid ....

c) A weak alkali ....

d) A neutral substance ....

e) A strong alkali ....

Neutralisation — A Useful Acid Reaction

Q1   Your stomach contains about a litre of acid which helps digest food. Occasionally some acid finds its way out of your stomach — this is called indigestion. It can be quite painful, but neutralisation can be used to cancel out the acid pain.

a)   Name a chemical substance which could be used to reduce the acid in your stomach.

    ....

b)   What is produced when the acid is neutralised?

    ....

c)   "Antacid" is the name given to the medicines which neutralise acids in the stomach.

Why are they called "antacids"?

    ....

d)   The general equation for these reactions has been started below.
Complete the equation by writing in the products.

Acid   +   Alkali   →   ....   + ...

Q2a) Complete the table below which shows the pH range that some plants prefer.

b)   What may cause the soil to get too acidic?

    ....
    ....
    ....

Plant	Soil pH which the plant likes
Potato	
Broccoli	
Carrot	
Onion	

c)   What will happen to a plant if the pH is wrong?

    ....

d)   "Lime" is used to neutralise acidic soil — what chemical substance is "lime"?

    ....

If you're stuck... see Page 71 of our KS3 Revision Guide (Levels 3-6) ☺

Less Useful Acid Reactions

Q1 **What is the natural pH of rain-water?**

....

Q2 Pollutants in the air make rain-water more acidic.

Will the pH of the rain-water go up or go down with pollutants in it?

....

Q3 **Give the name of two pollutants found in air which make rain-water more acidic.**

....

Q4 **Look at the two limestone statues below. One has been affected by acid rain, the other hasn't. Explain in as much detail as possible how and why each statue looks different.**

....

....

....

....

....

....

....

....

....

Q5 Stephen put an old tooth into a glass of cola. The next day he found that the tooth had turned soft and the surface of the tooth had been removed. He tested the pH of the drink and found that it was acidic.

What advice would you give to someone who drinks lots of cola everyday?

....

....

Static Charge

Q1   How would you use a duster to charge a plastic rod?

....

....

Q2   There are two types of charge; positive and negative.

Which type moves when an object is being charged up?

....

Q3   Electric charge can produce forces that pull things together (attract) or push them apart (repel). We call these forces electrostatic forces.

Complete the following table by writing whether the force between the two charges will "attract" or "repel" them.

Charge 1	Charge 2	Force between
positive	positive	
positive	negative	
negative	positive	
negative	negative	

charge!

taken out of the curriculum but still important

Q4   The gold leaf electroscope is a piece of equipment used to study static electric charge. The diagram shows a gold leaf electroscope that has no overall charge.

a)   When there is no overall charge on the gold leaf electroscope, will the leaves be open or closed?

....

b)   If some positive charge is brought up close to the top plate, will the leaves open or close?

....

c)   Suppose the top plate was charged so that the leaves were separated. How could you make the leaves move back together again?

....

....

Electricity and Current

Q1   What do we call a material that will carry an electric current?

electrical conducter

Q2   What do we call a material that won't carry an electric current?

electrical insulator

Q3   Put a tick by the materials below that will carry a current.

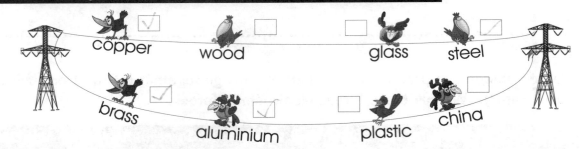

copper ☑   wood ☐   glass ☐   steel ☑
brass ☑   aluminium ☑   plastic ☐   china ☐

Q4   Circle the correct words to complete the following sentences.

Electric current is a flow of (charge) / *water*. It flows from *negative* / *positive*
to (negative) / *positive*. Conventional current flows from *negative* / *positive* to
negative / (positive).
For current to flow, a (power source) / *bulb* and a *bulb* / (complete circuit) are
needed. The current flowing out of a battery is (the same as) / *more than* the
current flowing back into it.

Q5   Look at the circuits below. Put a tick in the boxes by the bulbs that will light up.

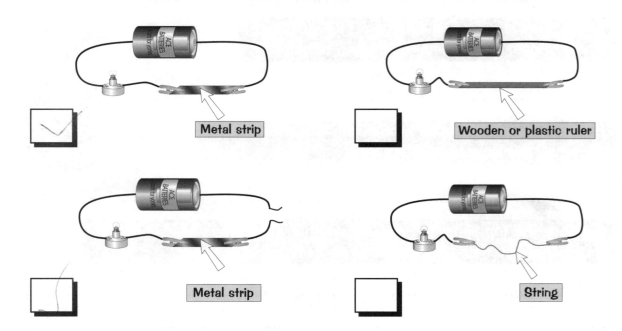

☑   Metal strip

☐   Wooden or plastic ruler

☐   Metal strip

☐   String

Electric Current in Circuits

Q1 Draw the symbols for the following devices. One is done for you.

Cell	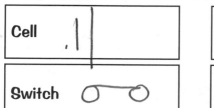
Switch	

Ammeter	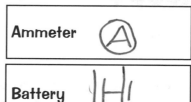
Battery	

Bulb	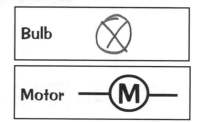
Motor	

Q2 An electric motor converts electrical energy to what type of energy?

...... kinetic ....

Q3 Study the following circuit diagrams and answer the questions below. All the lamps have the same resistance.

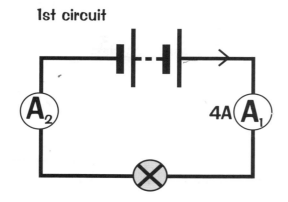

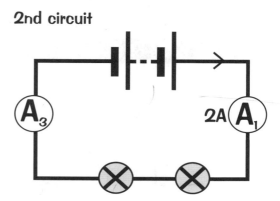

a) What is the value of the current flowing through A_2?

....

Resistance is futile!

b) What is the value of the current flowing through A_3?

....

c) Is the total resistance greater in the first circuit or the second?

....

Q4 What is meant by the term "short circuit"?

....

....

....

If you're stuck... see Page 76 of our KS3 Revision Guide (Levels 3-6) ☺

Magnets and Electromagnets

Q1 Name three magnetic elements.

1) .... 2) .... 3) ....

Q2 Draw the magnetic field lines for the magnet shown below.

Nice one!!

| N   S |

Q3 Beneath are shown two pairs of magnets without the poles labelled. One pair are attracting each other and the other pair are repelling each other.

Label the poles of the magnets "N" or "S" and draw the field lines.

Attracting   *Repelling*

Q4 Draw a diagram to show how you would make an electromagnet.

(You may use a *battery*, *wire* and an *iron cylinder*).

Force and Movement

Q1 | Circle the right formula used for calculating speed.

$$\text{Speed} = \frac{\text{Time}}{\text{Distance}} \qquad \text{Speed} = \frac{\text{Distance}}{\text{Time}}$$

$$\text{Speed} = \text{Time} \times \text{Distance}$$

Q2 | List the five things my toy car might do if it was acted on by an unbalanced force.

1) ....

2) ....

3) ....

4) ....

5) ....

Q3 | Circle the correct words to complete the following sentences.

Forces are measured in _kilograms_ / _newtons_. An unbalanced force is needed to _keep something_ / _start something_ moving. If all forces are balanced a moving object will _slow down_ / _keep going_. Weight is a type of _force_ / _mass_ and is measured in _newtons_ / _kilograms_.

Q4 | Spot is a stupid dog. Whenever he goes out for a walk with his owner, Lynda, he always starts pulling on his lead and tries to run off.

a) | Mark on the diagram which way Spot pulls and which way Lynda pulls.

b) | What will happen to Lynda and Spot if the lead breaks?

....

....

Air Resistance and Friction

Q1 Use arrows to mark on the truck the following forces.
(It is going forwards).

> Driving force,   Friction,
> Weight,   Reaction of road.

a) If the car's engine failed at 70 mph on the motorway which force would vanish?

....

b) What would friction do to the speed of the car after the engine failed?

....

Q2 The pictures below show the fall of a parachutist from an aeroplane.

a) For each part of the skydive draw pairs of arrows to show how the vertical forces
act on the parachutist. Use big arrows to represent big forces.

JUMP!

Getting faster

Steady speed

Getting slower

Steady speed

Stopped

b) Which is greater, the drag force when free falling at steady speed or the drag force
with the parachute open at steady speed?

....

Force and Rotation

Q1 Machines are things that make tasks easier. Machines can be very simple. The prize for the simplest goes to the ramp but a close runner-up is the lever.

Which person will find it easiest to lift their rock? Circle your choice.

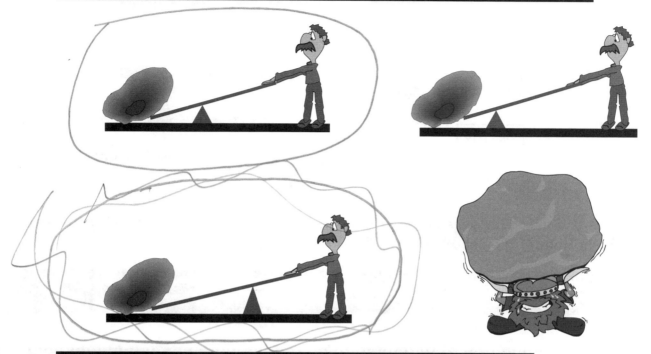

Q2 **Circle the correct words to complete the following sentences.**

When you are using a lever, the longer the lever on your side of the pivot the _greater_ / (_smaller_) the turning force about the pivot. Using a long lever with the pivot close to the load makes lifting a large load _harder_ / (_easier._) Using a long lever with the pivot close to the load makes the distance moved by the load (_small_) / _large_.

Q3 **Mark on each of the following diagrams the loads, efforts and pivots.**

An example has been done for you.

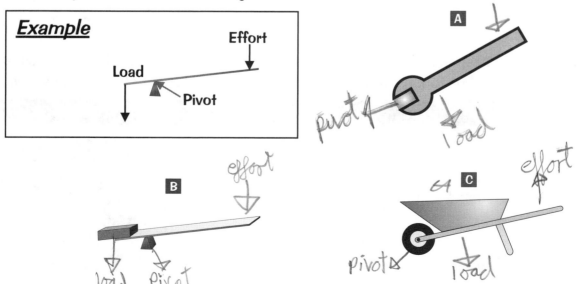

Example

Effort
Load
Pivot

If you're stuck... see Page 84 of our KS3 Revision Guide (Levels 3-6) ☺

62

<u>Pressure</u>

Q1 In modern tank guns the projectile (bullet) is held in a wide bottomed cup called a sabot, inside the barrel. When the projectile leaves the barrel the sabot breaks away as the projectile heads towards the target.

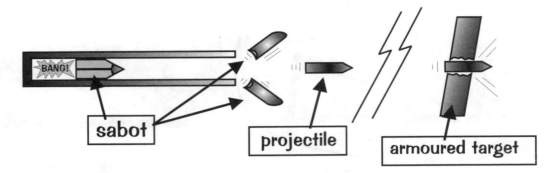

a) If there is a maximum pressure that the gun barrel can stand then changing the area of the bottom of the sabot will alter the force on the projectile.

If the area of the bottom of the sabot is increased, will the force acting on it from the bang increase or decrease?

....

b) What effect will this have on the speed of the bullet as it leaves the barrel?

....

c) If the bullet is to penetrate a target, is it better for the bullet to be narrow or thick? Why?

....

....

Q2 Big Foot and his mate Little Foot had a race across the Himalayas. Big Foot weighs more than Little Foot but to the surprise of them both, Little Foot got stuck in the snow.

Explain in terms of pressure why it was Little Foot who got stuck and not Big Foot.

....

....

....

....

Properties of Light

Q1 Circle the correct word in the brackets to complete the sentence.

"Light always travels in (curved / **straight**) lines."

Taken out of the curriculum but still important

Q2 In the picture a torch is shining light on to a man and casting a shadow.

Put the following labels in the white boxes.

No light

Q3 Explain how shadows are formed.

....

....

....

Q4 We see non-luminous objects because light reflects off them and enters our eyes.
Look at the picture below and show the path of a ray of light from the light source so Pedro can see the bird.

Light source

Pedro

bird

If you're stuck... see Page 88 of our KS3 Revision Guide (Levels 3-6) ☺

Reflection

Q1 The diagram shows light rays about to be reflected from a smooth surface.

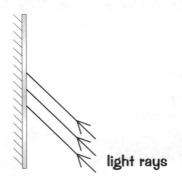

light rays

a) Complete the diagram to show how the light rays are reflected from this surface.

b) Name a type of reflector with a smooth surface.

....

Q2 The diagram shows light rays about to be reflected from a rough surface.

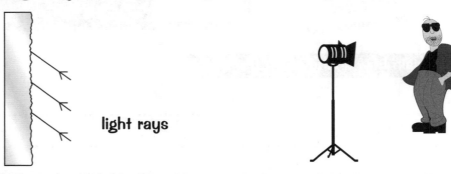

light rays

a) Complete the diagram to show how the light rays are reflected from this surface.

b) Most reflectors have rough surfaces.

Give two examples of a reflector with a rough surface.

....

c) What type of reflection would you get from a piece of sandpaper?

....

Q3 List three uses of mirrors.

1) ....

2) ....

3) ....

Refraction

Q1 In physics, what is a medium?

....

Q2 When light enters glass from air it changes direction.
What is this change of direction called?

....

Q3 Glass is denser than air so light will refract when it enters and leaves a glass block.
The diagrams show rays of light in air entering a glass block. For each one complete the path of the ray of light into and out of the block.

a)

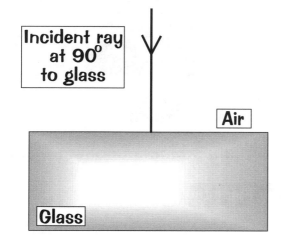

b)

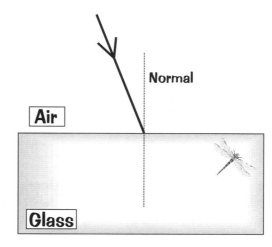

Q4 Circle the correct words in the brackets to complete the following sentences.

a) When a light ray travels from one medium into another, more dense, medium, it bends (away from / towards) the normal.

b) When a light ray travels from one medium into another, less dense, medium, it bends (away from / towards) the normal.

Colour

Q1   When white light passes through a prism it is split up into different colours.

a)   **What name is given to this "splitting up" of white light?**

....

b)   The picture shows white light passing through a prism and landing on a white screen.

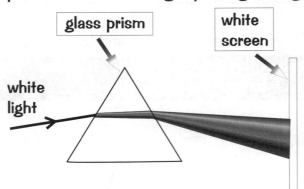

Write down the name for the "rainbow of colours" produced.

....

c)   **Tick the seven colours that you would see on the screen.**

magenta	☐	pink	☐	gold	☐	black	☐
yellow	☐	red	☐	cyan	☐	green	☐
indigo	☐	blue	☐	violet	☐	orange	☐

Q2   The diagram shows white light being passed through a coloured filter.

a)   **Write down the colour of the filter.**

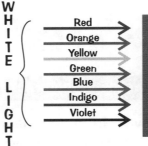
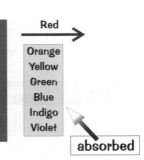

....

b)   **Explain your answer.**

....

....

If you're stuck... see Page 91 of our KS3 Revision Guide (Levels 3-6) ☺   *Physical Processes*

Sound

Q1 The picture shows a demonstration of sound travel using a bell jar.

a) **Complete the sentences by circling the correct words in brackets.**

"When air is sucked out of the jar the ringing of
the alarm clock inside the jar gets (louder /
quieter). When all the air is removed the bell
(can not be heard / stops)."

b) **The ring of the alarm clock goes quiet because: (tick the correct box)**

there is no air in the jar to carry the vibrations ☐

sound can not travel through the glass of the bell jar ☐

the vacuum stops the bell moving ☐

Q2 Sound waves have many properties in common with light waves.
— e.g. sound diffracts *and* light diffracts.

Give two other physical properties that sound and light have in common.

1) ....

2) ....

Q3 Sound waves can be displayed on an oscilloscope screen like the one below.

a) **Which of the lines in the picture indicate the amplitude of the wave?**

....

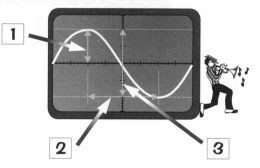

b) A wave with the same frequency but carrying
more energy than the first one is fed into the
oscilloscope.

i) **Draw how the wave will look on the screen opposite.**

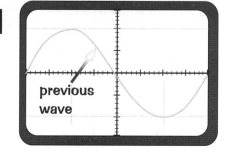

previous wave

ii) **What difference would you hear?**

....

If you're stuck... see Page 92 of our KS3 Revision Guide (Levels 3-6) ☺

Hearing

Q1   The picture below shows how sound from a twanged ruler travels to the brain.

Use the following words to complete the labelling in the diagram.

particles   ruler   bones   drum   hairs   brain   cochlea

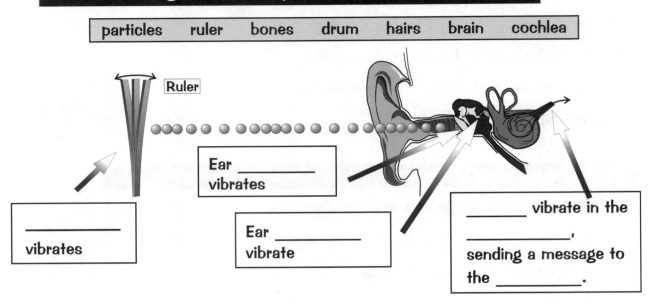

Ruler

Ear _____ vibrates

_____ vibrates

Ear _____ vibrate

_____ vibrate in the _____, sending a message to the _____.

Q2   The bar chart shows the range of frequencies that people and animals can hear.

a) **Who has the most limited range of hearing?**

....

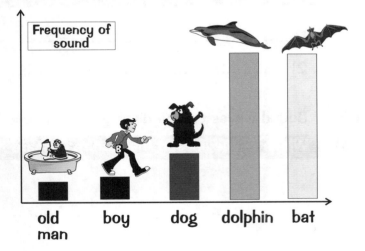

Frequency of sound

old man   boy   dog   dolphin   bat

b) **Suggest a reason why dolphins need to hear such high frequency sounds.**

....

....

....

c) **Tick the correct box below to complete the following.**

"Dolphins can hear higher frequency sounds than dogs. This means that dolphins can hear sounds of a ...."

lower pitch [ ]   higher pitch [ ]

The Moon and Satellites

Q1 **What is a satellite?**

....

Q2 **Which of the following are satellites? Tick the correct boxes.**

The Moon ☐   The Sun ☐   The Earth ☐   The Hubble Space Telescope ☐

Q3 **Give two uses of an artificial satellite orbiting the Earth.**

1) ....

2) ....

Q4 **What is the name of the force that keeps the Moon in orbit around the Earth?**

....

Q5 The picture shows the Earth and the Moon in space.

Use two arrows to show the force of the Earth's pull on the Moon and the force of the Moon's pull on the Earth.

Q6 **Fill the gaps in the following sentences. Use the words in the "nebula". Words may be used once, more than once or not at all.**

moon 28 38 Sun colour shape refracting reflecting different same light dark

The _____ orbits the Earth in _____ days.

The Moon appears to change _____ as it goes through a full orbit of

the Earth. This is because we only see the part of the Moon which is

_____ light from the Sun. We see _____ amounts of

the Moon's sunny side as it orbits the Earth — that's why it seems to change shape

because you can't see the _____ bits.

Day and Night

Q1   The picture shows the Earth.

Earth

a)   Complete the labelling for "night-time" and "daytime".

b)   Draw the Earth's rotational axis on the picture.

c)   How long does it take for the Earth to rotate once on its axis? (Give your answer in hours).

....

Q2   Explain why we experience daytime and night-time on Earth.

....

....

....

Q3   Reginald lives in Scotland. He sees the Sun moving across the sky during the day.

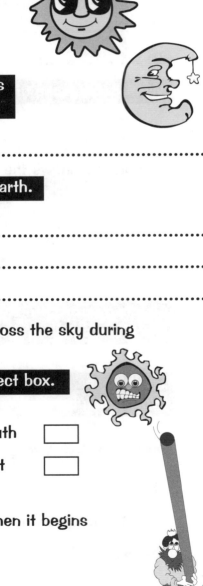

a)   Where does the Sun rise in the morning? Tick the correct box.

in the North ☐   in the South ☐

in the West ☐   in the East ☐

b)   He sees the Sun reaching its highest point in the sky, then it begins to descend.

At what time does it begin to descend?

....

The Four Seasons

Q1 The picture below shows the Earth in four positions in its orbit around the Sun.

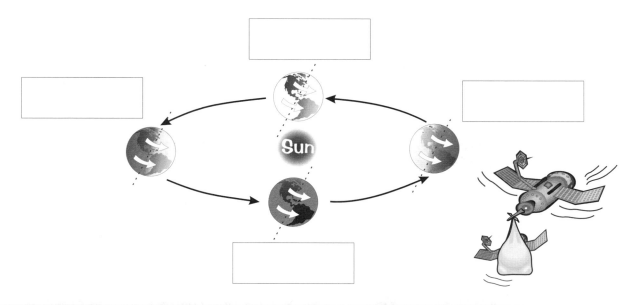

a) Label the four seasons on the diagram, for the Northern Hemisphere.

b) Shadows cast at midday are shortest during one of the seasons.

i) Which season is this?

....

ii) Explain why shadows are *generally* shortest in this season.

....

....

Q2 The Earth's axis is tilted and this is why we have seasons.
However, if there was no tilt, the countries near the equator would still have a warmer climate than countries further north or south.

Use the picture below to help explain why this would be the case.

....

....

....

....

....

....

....

Earth ┊

Sun's rays

The Solar System

Q1 **Is Earth a planet or a star?**

....

Q2 **Is the Sun a planet or a star?**

....

Q3 **What is the main difference between a star and a planet?**

....

....

Q4 The eight planets of our solar system are shown in the picture below.

Write in the names of the planets in the spaces provided.

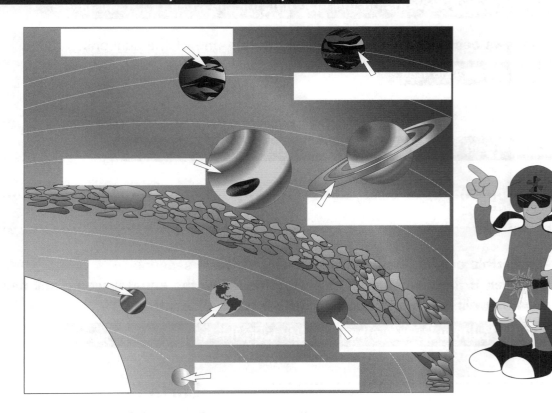

Q5 All the planets move around the Sun which lies at the centre of the Solar System.

What is the name given to the path followed by a planet going around the Sun?

....

Q6 **What is the name given to the shape of a planet's path around the Sun?**

....

The Solar System

Q7 What is the name of the force that keeps planets in orbit about the Sun?

....

Q8 Look at the table of data below. It shows information about the planets.

	PLANET	RELATIVE SIZE	RELATIVE MASS	MEAN DIST. FROM SUN	ORBIT TIME
INNER PLANETS	MERCURY	0.4	0.05	58	88d
	VENUS	0.9	0.8 (Earth	108 (millions	225d d=Earth
	EARTH	1.0	1.0 masses)	150 of km)	365d days
	MARS	0.5	0.1	228	687d
OUTER PLANETS	JUPITER	11.0	318.0	778	12y
	SATURN	9.4	95.0	1430	29y y=Earth
	URANUS	4.0	15.0	2870	84y years
	NEPTUNE	3.8	17.0	4500	165y

a) Which planet is nearest to the Sun?

....

b) Which planet has the most mass?

....

c) Which planet has the least mass?

....

d) Which planet takes the longest time to orbit the Sun?

....

e) Complete the following sentence by circling the correct word.

The orbit time of planets _increases_ / _decreases_ as the distance from the Sun increases.

Q9 The asteroid belt lies between which two planets?

....

Q10 Which of the following objects are located in the Solar system?
Circle the correct ones.

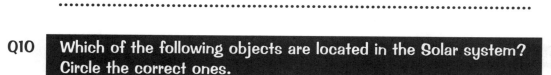

Stars   Comets   Asteroids   Galaxies   Planets   Moons

Types of Energy and Energy Transfer

Q1 The pictures below show examples of the eight main types of energy.

Write down the names of the energy types shown in each picture below.
Use the words given in the grey box below.

light, kinetic, sound, elastic potential,
gravitational potential, chemical, electrical, heat

....

....

....

Q2 Complete the diagram below by labelling the arrows. Use words
like "energy input", "useful energy output" and "wasted energy".

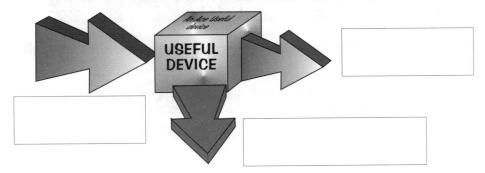

Is it possible to build a machine that doesn't waste any energy?

....

Energy Resources

The Sun is the source of most of the energy resources on the Earth.

Q1 Complete the energy diagrams below by writing the name of the final energy resource in the spaces provided. Use the words given in the grey box below.

> wave power, wind power, chemical (batteries), chemical (wood), fossil fuel

a)

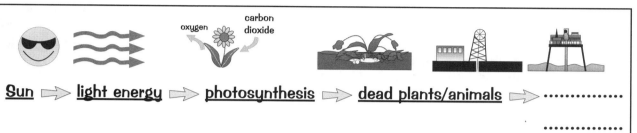

Sun ⟹ light energy ⟹ photosynthesis ⟹ dead plants/animals ⟹ ....
....

b)

Sun ⟹ heats atmosphere ⟹ causes winds ⟹
....

c)

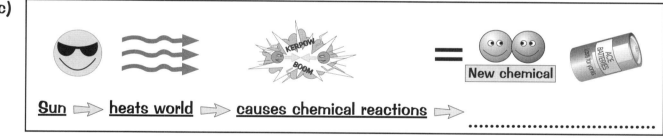

Sun ⟹ heats world ⟹ causes chemical reactions ⟹
....

d)

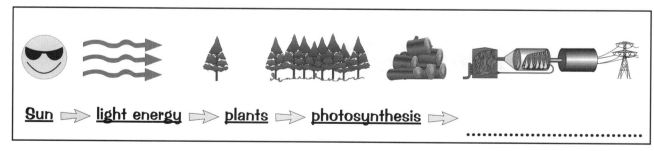

Sun ⟹ light energy ⟹ plants ⟹ photosynthesis ⟹
....

e)

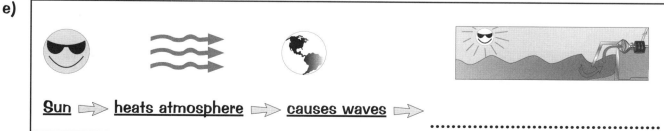

Sun ⟹ heats atmosphere ⟹ causes waves ⟹
....

If you're stuck... see Page 101 of our KS3 Revision Guide (Levels 3-6) ☺

Generating Electricity

Q1 The diagram below shows how chemical energy can be converted to electrical energy.

Boiler   Turbine   Generator

Fuel   Grid

| Chemical energy | → | Heat energy | → | Kinetic energy | → | Electrical energy |

a) **Name three types of fuel that can be used for the boiler.**

1) .... 2) .... 3) ....

b) **Are these energy sources "renewable" or "non-renewable"?**

1) .... 2) .... 3) ....

c) **Why isn't petrol burned in power stations?**

....

Q2 **Name two things people could do to help preserve non-renewable fuels.**

1) ....

2) ....

Q3 Other ways to produce electricity involve the use of renewable energy resources. Most of these get their energy from the Sun.

Name the four forms of renewable energy shown in the three pictures.

....

....

....

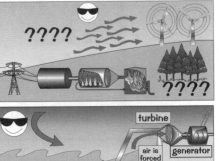

????   ????

?????

Solar panel

turbine

generator

air is forced out

water wave moves in

????

Not caterpillars

Q4 **Name a renewable energy resource that can be burnt.**

....

The Answers

Life Processes and Living Things

Page 2 — Life Processes and Cells

Q1 growth, sensitivity, nutrition, movement, respiration, excretion, reproduction

Q2 1. nucleus
2. cytoplasm
3. cell membrane

Q3 1. nucleus
2. cytoplasm
3. cell membrane
4. cell wall
5. vacuole
6. chloroplast

Page 3 — Plant Organs

Q1 1. flower
2. stem
3. leaf
4. root

Q2 flower

Q3 leaf

Q4 a) water and minerals
b) to anchor it in place

Q5 chloroplasts of chlorophyll

Page 4 — Specialised Cells and Organs

Q1 a) locomotion
b) genetic information/genes
c) They enable the sperm to break through the cell membrane of the egg in order to fertilise it.

Q2 water, minerals

Q3 a) cell → tissue → organ → organism
b) yes

Page 5 — Human Organ System

Q1 nervous, muscles, reproductive, glands, digestive, circulatory, excretory, respiratory, skeleton

Q2 1. nose
2. tongue
3. eye
4. ear
5. skin

Q3 respiratory system

Q4 a) support, movement
b) It protects your brain.

Page 6 — Nutrition

Q1 carbohydrates, proteins, fats, minerals, vitamins, water, roughage

Q2 meat / eggs / fish

Q3 minerals

Q4 They are the best source of energy.

Q5 Body tissue is mostly water. A lot of water is lost in maintaining body temperature, breathing and excretion.

Page 7 — Digestion

Q1 Breaking down of large, mostly insoluble food molecules into small soluble food molecules for absorption.

Q2 mechanical grinding of food, chemical break-down

Q3

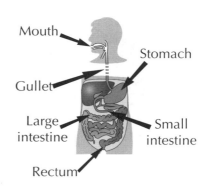

Page 8 — Absorption in the Gut

Q1 Enzymes are used to **break up** big molecules so that small ones can be made. These smaller molecules **can** pass through the gut wall into the blood. They then pass **into** the cells and are used by the body.

Q2 starch — carbohydrase
protein — protease
fats — lipase

Q3 small intestine

Q4 large intestine

Q5 They are finger-like projections with a copious blood supply and thin walls enabling efficient absorption.

Page 9 — The Circulatory System

Q1 1. **Deoxygenated** blood enters the heart.
2. It's then pumped to the lungs to pick up some **oxygen**.
3. It's now **oxygenated** and travels back to the **heart**.
4. It's then **pumped** around the body so every cell gets the vital **oxygen** that it needs.
The sequence then repeats from step number **1**.

Q2 These have thin walls which help food particles etc. to pass through — **capillaries**.
These carry blood at low pressure back to the heart — **veins**.
These carry blood at high pressure away from the heart — **arteries**.

Page 10 — Skeleton, Joints and Muscles

Q1 support, protection, movement

Q2 a) It supports the body. It protects the spinal column. It flexes allowing body motion.
b) It protects the heart and lungs. It supports the muscles for breathing. It allows the chest to expand and contract.

Q3 immovable — skull
slightly movable — spine
freely movable — knee

Q4 Muscles work in **pairs** against each other. One muscle contracts while the other **one** relaxes (lengthens), and vice versa. **Tendons** attach the muscles to the bones. One **muscle** pulls the bone in one direction and the other pulls it in the **opposite** direction.

Page 11 — Growing Up

Q1

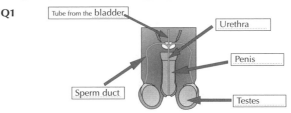

The Answers

Q2

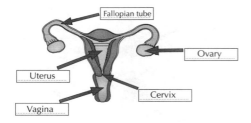

Q3 The lining of the uterus starts to build up again — **day 4**.
The wall remains thick awaiting the arrival of a fertilised egg— **days 14-28**.
An egg is released from the ovaries of the female— **day 14**.
Bleeding starts as the lining of the uterus (the womb) breaks down and passes out of the vagina— **day 28**.

Page 12 — Having a Baby

Q1

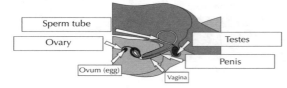

Q2 1. Ovulation
2. Copulation
3. Fertilisation
4. Cell division
5. Implantation

Q3

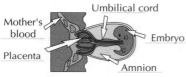

Q4 The embryo has a brain, heart, eyes and legs — **1 month**.
It kicks and it's pesky finger nails can be felt — **5 months**.
The foetus is viable — **7 months**.
The baby is fully developed — **9 months**.

Page 13 — Breathing

Q1

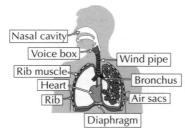

Q2 The **oxygen** we need to stay alive comes from the **air** which enters our **lungs**. The waste gases, **carbon dioxide** and water vapour leave our body and the whole process is called **breathing**. The important gas we take in is absorbed into our **blood** and is used with sugar in the cells to give us **energy**.

Q3 a) Ribs move **up and out**.
Diaphragm moves **down**.
Volume of chest **increases**.
Air rushes **in**.

b) Ribs move **down and in**.
Diaphragm moves **up**.
Volume of chest **decreases**.
Air rushes **out**.

Page 14 — Smoking

Q1 a) The temperature rises alarmingly.
b) The glass wool turns black/brown with tar.

Q2

Type of Grot	What the Grot does to the body
nicotine	Is an addictive drug that raises the heart beat rate, narrows the arteries and causes high blood pressure. This leads to <u>HEART DISEASE.</u>
Tar	Coats lining of lungs reducing efficiency etc.
carbon monoxide	This is a <u>poisonous gas</u> which joins up with red blood cells making them incapable of transporting OXYGEN around the body.

Q3 E.g. various cancers, heart disease, shortness of breath, reduced sense of smell/taste, increased frequency of colds

Page 15 — Respiration

Q1 **G**lucose + **O**xygen = **C**arbon **d**ioxide + **W**ater + **E**nergy
Q2 a) Water vapour is breathed out from moist lungs and condenses in cold U-tube.
b) Breath contains carbon dioxide that is produced by respiration.
Q3 cell division, growth, maintaining body temperature, play, repair, work

Page 16 — Health

Q1 a) The absence of **infection**.
b) Eating a balanced **diet**.
c) Doing enough **exercise**.
d) Not abusing **drugs/body**.
Q2 Alcohol is a **depressant**, despite the fact that it may give a **happy** feeling. It's a **poison** which affects the **brain** and **liver** leading to various health problems.
Solvents are drugs because they cause hallucinations, which are illusions of the **mind**. Solvents can have psychological effects on the **character** and **behaviour** of the abuser. They also cause serious damage to the **brain/liver/lungs/kidneys**, the **brain/liver/lungs/kidneys**, **brain/liver/lungs/kidneys** and **brain/liver/lungs/kidneys**.
Q3 Hallucinogens — Examples: Ecstasy and LSD.
Pain Killers — Examples: Heroin and Morphine.
Stimulants — Examples: Amphetamine (speed) and Methedrine.
Depressants — Example: Barbiturates.

Page 17 — Fighting Disease

Q1 The body has its own **natural defences** against disease but it can be helped by **medicines** and **immunisation**. The main armies of defence of the body are **antibodies** and **white blood cells** which are part of the body's **immune** system.
Q2 bacteria only

The Answers

Q3   bacteria — e.g. tetanus, whooping cough
          viruses — e.g. AIDS, 'flu'

Q4

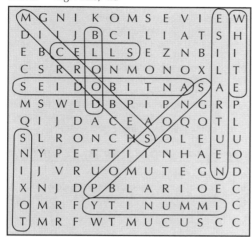

Page 18 — How Plants Make Food

Q1   food / glucose

Q2   carbon dioxide + water $\xrightarrow[\text{chlorophyll}]{\text{SUNLIGHT}}$ glucose + oxygen

Q3   1. light
          2. chlorophyll
          3. water
          4. carbon dioxide

Q4 a) carbon dioxide
  b)   oxygen
  c)   water

Page 19 — Photosynthesis

Q1   No photosynthesis happens in the dark. The starch had been used up and not replaced.

Q2

Page 20 — Plant Growth

Q1   large surface area to volume ratio, thin walls

Q2   Nitrates — Provide nitrogen which is needed for making proteins.
          Phosphates — Provide phosphorous which is needed for photosynthesis and respiration.
          Potassium — Helps enzymes to work properly.

Q3   A small plant with yellow older leaves. — This plant is lacking **nitrates**.
          Poor root growth and purple younger leaves. — This plant is lacking **phosphates**.
          Yellow leaves with dead bits. — This plant is lacking **potassium**.

Page 21 — Plant Reproduction

Q1

Q2   stamen

Q3   carpel

Q4   the female sex cell in plants is called — the ova
          the female sex organ in plants is called — the carpel
          the female sex organ is made up from — the stigma, style and ovary
          the male sex cell in plants is called — the pollen
          the male sex organ in plants is called — the stamen
          the male sex organ is made up from — the filament and anther

Q5   A — large petals, scented flower, nectaries, insect pollinated
          B — small dull petals long filaments, wind pollinated

Page 22 — Plant Reproduction and Seeds

Q1   Wind dispersed — sycamore, dandelion
          Dispersed by animals — burdock, tomato
          Dispersed by explosion — pea

Q2   temperature, air conditions, water supply

Q3

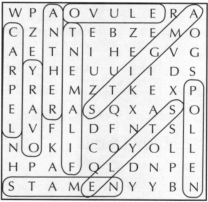

The two other words are **stam**en and **c**arp**el**.

Page 23 — The Carbon Cycle

Q1 a) burning and respiration
  b)   via the food chain / animals eat plants
  c)   ancient plant and animal remains

Page 24 — Inherited and Environmental Variation

Q1   The following should be ticked:
          blue eyes, red hair, blood group A positive, strong legs

Q2 a) environmental (probably)
  b)   temperature, soil quality, watering, light, size of pot, genetic variation in seeds
  c)   Try to replicate exactly the conditions in which his father's flower did so well.

Page 25 — Classification

Q1   The following should be ticked:
          shark, snake, tortoise, dog
          The following should have a cross:
          slug, butterfly

The Answers

Q2 newt — amphibian
dragonfly — insect
frog — amphibian
goldfish — fish
snail — mollusc
pond skater — insect

Q3 Birds and mammals have backbones and so belong to the **vertebrate** group of animals. Birds have **feathers**, **wings** and a beak while mammals have **fur** or hair and **four** limbs. **Mammals** give birth to live young unlike **birds** which lay eggs.

Page 26 — Using Keys

Q1 A — Grabbing Flappoid
B — Standard Moonoid
C — Armless Flappoid
D — Easy Listenoid

Q2

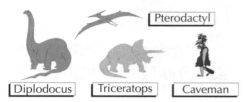

Diplodocus   Triceratops   Caveman   Pterodactyl

Page 27 — Adaptation

Q1 Polar bears have special features to help them live in **arctic** conditions. They have a thick layer of **fat** and a thick fur coat to keep them **warm**. Their **rounded** shape gives them a small surface area to reduce **heat loss**.

Q2 Camels can **drink** and **store** lots of water which is handy for those long dry spells.
Fat is stored in its **hump** to assist the loss of heat from the rest of its body.
Big, wide **feet** stop it from sinking in the soft **sand**.

Page 28 — Food Chains

Q1 a) transfer of biomass and energy
b) worm
c) cat (The chain shown gives bird too but birds are more likely to be omnivores.)

Q2 carnivores — animals that eat other animals
omnivores — animals that can eat both plants and animals
herbivores — animals that eat plants
consumers — organisms that rely on other organisms for their food
producers — organisms that can make their own food

Q3 carnivore, consumer, food chain, omnivore, producer, herbivore

Page 29 — Food Webs

Q1 a) Otter — **Top** c**a**rnivore
Pike — **Tert**iary c**o**nsumer
Perch — Sec**ond**ary Cons**um**er
Water beetle — P**rim**ary **cons**umer
Waterweed — Pro**duc**er
b) tadpoles and water beetles
c) minnows, perch, pike and otters
d) tadpoles and water beetles
e) There will be **more** water beetles so the waterweed will be eaten **more**. The minnows will have **more** food but will be eaten **more** by the pike.

Page 30 — Problems in Food Chains

Q1 a) Grass → Rabbits → Fox
b) It tells us the numbers of each species in a community.
c) It might get concentrated as it is passed up the food chain.

Q2

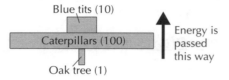

Blue tits (10)
Caterpillars (100)
Oak tree (1)
Energy is passed this way

Page 31 — Survival

Q1 a) their claws
b) B. It has bigger claws.
c) In a population of lobsters the individuals which are most like **lobster B** would survive best. This means that they are more likely to **reproduce** and pass their **genes** on to their young. Gradually the whole population would become more and more like **lobster B**.

Materials and Their Properties

Page 32 — Types of Material

Q1 a) Metal is strong, easily shaped, tough and abundant.
b) Plastics are abundant, cheap, insulators and easy to mould.
c) Glass is a transparent, cheap and abundant insulator with a high melting point.
d) Fibres can be woven into cloth. They are tough, and can be natural or man-made.
e) Ceramics are cheap and strong in compression.

Q2 Means that the materials can be used over and over again, where facilities exist.

Q3 Steel is good in tension and concrete is good in compression.

Page 33 — Materials and their Properties

Q1 Window pane — transparent, insulator, hard
Steel girder — strong, hard, flexible

Q2 Rubber is flexible, strong, and is able to absorb bumps in the road. It is easy to mould into the tyre shape with tread.

Q3 Non-metals are usually poor conductors of heat. The handle helps to insulate the user from the heat of the pan on the stove.

Q4 toffee bar — tasty
electrical plug casing — insulator
compass needle — magnetic
horse shoe — malleable when heated
diamond — hard

The Answers

Pages 34-35 — Solids, Liquids and Gases

Q1
Cheese — solid
Treacle — liquid
Steam — gas
Jelly — solid
Glass — liquid
Petrol — liquid
Paper — solid
Dry Air — gas

Q2

Q3
A — solid
B — liquid
C — gas

Q4 This tells us that the density of ice is less than the density of water. Most substances are denser in solid state.

Q5 Solids, liquids and gases all have different **spacings** between their particles. The particles in a gas are quite **far** apart compared to the particles in liquids and solids. Because of this, it is very easy to **compress** a gas but not so easy to do the same to a liquid or solid. **Liquids** will take the shape of any container they are put in, whereas **solids** keep their shape. Finally, **gases** will **expand** to fill any available space in a container.

Pages 36-37 — Physical Changes

Q1
1. Melting
2. Freezing
3. Boiling
4. Condensing

Q2 Solid. Particles are very close initially and strong bonds need to be broken.

Q3 The energy causes the particles to move further and further apart from one another and vibrate more.

Q4 Diffusion is the random spreading out of particles in space. The 'smell' particles will be in gaseous form, and as they are constantly moving, the smell spreads.

Q5

Q6
The name being given to the solid being dissolved — solute
The liquid that the solid is being dissolved into — solvent
The name given to the mixture of the dissolving solid and liquid — solution
If the solid will dissolve, it is known as — soluble
But if the solid won't dissolve, it is known as — insoluble
If the liquid won't allow you to dissolve any more solid in it, it is — saturated
The amount of solid a liquid will allow to dissolve in it — solubility

Q7

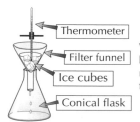

Wait until the ice begins to melt, then read off the temperature from the thermometer

Page 38 — Atoms and Elements

Q1
Carbon — E
My pet hamster — N
Air — N
Uranium — E
All Saints — N
Helium — E
Nitrogen — E
Carbon dioxide — C

Q2 A group is a vertical column of elements. A period is a horizontal row of elements.

Q3 Elements consist of one type of **atom**. Elements can't be split up into anything simpler by **chemical** methods. There are about **100** different elements. Each one has a name and a shorthand **symbol**, e.g. Carbon, C. Everything on Earth is made up of **elements**. The Periodic Table is made up of groups and periods. Some groups have names, such as group 1, the **alkali** metals, group 7, the **halogens** and group 0, the **noble** gases.

Q4 The following should be ticked:

Page 39 — Compounds

Q1 An element can not be broken down any further. Compounds contain more than one element, chemically combined in fixed proportions.

Q2 Elements — sulphur, lead, oxygen, helium, calcium, chlorine
Compounds — magnesium oxide, sodium chloride, water, carbon dioxide, sulphur dioxide, carbon monoxide, sulphuric acid

Q3 carbon dioxide — carbon and oxygen
copper sulphate — copper, sulphur, oxygen

Q4 iron, sulphur and oxygen — iron sulphate
hydrogen and sulphur — hydrogen sulphide

Page 40 — Properties of Metals

Q1

Q2 Metals are good conductors and have high densities and melting points. Non-metals are poor conductors and are found on the right hand side of the periodic table, etc.

Q3 Shiny
Malleable
Sonorous
Magnetic (some)

The Answers

Q4   1. C
      2. D
      3. H
      4. G
      5. F
      6. B
      7. A
      8. E

Page 41 — Properties of Non-metals

Q1   Non-metals are commonly gases at room temperature. This tells us that particles are widely spaced, have poor bonding, etc.

Q2   ship — brittle
         balloons — low density
         bus — poor conductors
         brush — soft

Q3 a), **b)** and **c)**

Element	Symbol	Melting Point (°C)	Boiling Point (°C)	State at 20°C
Sulphur	S	112	444	solid
Oxygen	O	-218	-183	gas
Bromine	Br	-7	58	liquid ✓
Neon	Ne	-248	-246	gas
Iodine	I	114	183	solid

   d)   Most non-metals are gases at room temperature.

Pages 42-43 — Mixtures

Q1   Several substances combined. Separable by physical means.

Q2   Filtration
         Evaporation
         Chromatography
         Distillation

Q3 a)   To aid the condensation of the water.
   b)   By checking its boiling point is 100°C (or add anhydrous copper sulphate — turns blue with water).
   c)   The water in the ink boils off, cools and is then collected.

Q4 a)   two
   b)   an organic solvent
   c)   The unknown composition of the suspect's paint is being compared to the composition of the paint on Clive's car.
   d)   three

Pages 44-45 — Geological Changes

Q1

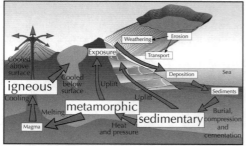

Q2   Over millions of years rocks change from one type to another. This is called the **rock cycle**. Rocks are broken up by **weathering** and washed into the **sea**. Over millions of years these become buried, **compressed** and cemented and form sedimentary rocks. Sometimes these rocks become **buried** deeper into the Earth, and are changed by **heat** and pressure into **metamorphic** rocks. If metamorphic rocks are buried still further they can **melt** and become **magma**. Pressure forces the **magma** upwards where it **cools** to make **igneous** rocks.

Q3   Igneous rocks form from **cooled down magma**.
         Sedimentary rocks form from **layers of sediment compressed and cemented over millions of years**.
         Metamorphic rocks form from **compressed and heated sedimentary rock.**

Q4   Basalt — igneous
         Chalk — sedimentary
         Slate — metamorphic
         Grit — sedimentary
         Granite — igneous
         Marble — metamorphic
         Obsidian — igneous
         Sandstone — sedimentary
         Marl — sedimentary
         Quartzite — metamorphic

Page 46 — Useful Chemical Change

Q1 a)   True
   b)   False
   c)   False
   d)   True
   e)   True
   f)   False
   g)   False

Q2 a)   It gives out energy in the form of heat.
   b)   It can make alcohol, medicines and bread.
   c)   It extracts metals from their ores.
   d)   It removes acid or alkali (in the stomach for example).
   e)   It can extract metals from their ores.

Page 47 — Less Useful Chemical Change

Q3 a)

Tube	Colour of nail before	Colour of nail after
1	steel colour	brown/rusty
2	steel colour	no change
3	steel colour	no change

   b)   tube 1
   c)   It removes water in case the air is moist.
   d)   Oxygen and water

Q4   Oil it — this repels air and water
         Paint it — paint covers the surface
         Galvanise it — the surface is covered in zinc

Page 48 — Reactions of Metals

Q1 a) 1. potassium
        2. iron
        3. copper
   b)   Copper — it doesn't react with water.

   c)

Reaction in acid	Potassium	Copper	Iron
Observations	Fizzed violently, tube became very hot.	Metal sank to bottom, no reaction.	Bubbles appeared slowly on the metal.

Page 49 — Displacement Reactions

Q1 a)   yes
   b)   more
   c)   no
   d)   less
   e)   yes
   f)   more
   g)   displacement reaction
   h)   magnesium, X, iron, copper

The Answers

Pages 50-51 — Acids and Alkalis

Q1 All acids are dangerous — False
All alkalis are dangerous — False
All acids are dissolved in water — True
All alkalis are dissolved in water — True
Acids can burn skin — True
Alkalis feel soapy — True
Lemons contain alkali — False
Acids taste sweet — False
Acids stop indigestion — False
All acids are corrosive — False
Acids have a pH above 7 — False
Acids have a pH below 7 — True
The pH scale goes from 0 to 14 — False

Q2 E.g. hydrochloric acid, sulphuric acid, nitric acid

Q3 E.g. sodium hydroxide, calcium hydroxide, potassium oxide

Q4

Q5

Q6 E.g. wear protective clothing, do not touch, do not spill

Q7 The following should be ticked:
pickled onions, car batteries, ant stings

Q8 The following should be ticked:
oven cleaner, soaps, fertilisers, lime

Q9 Hydrogen — use a lighted splint, listen for the squeaky pop.
Carbon dioxide — turns limewater cloudy.

Page 52 — The pH Scale and Indicators

Q1 Special dye that changes colour depending on how acidic or alkaline something is.

Q2

pH 1 2 3 4 5 6 7 8 9 10 11 12 13 14

red	green	purple

ACIDS — — — NEUTRAL — — ALKALIS

Q3 a) 3
b) 14
c) 14
d) 7
e) 1

Q4 a) hydrogen chloride
b) ethanoic acid
c) magnesium oxide
d) potassium chloride
e) potassium hydroxide

Page 53 — Neutralisation — A Useful Acid Reaction

Q1 a) magnesium oxide
b) salt and water
c) They are anti-acids, i.e. they combat acidity.
d) acid + alkali ➔ salt + **water**

Q2 a) Potato — 5
Broccoli — 5 / 6
Carrot — 6
Onion — 6 / 7
b) acid rain
c) It won't grow properly.
d) calcium hydroxide

Page 54 — Less Useful Acid Reactions

Q1 6
Q2 down
Q3 sulphur dioxide, oxides of nitrogen
Q4 The statue on the right has suffered from acid rain weathering. The statues are made of limestone, which is calcium carbonate. Acid in the rain reacts with this to form soluble calcium salts, carbon dioxide and water. So the statue just gets 'eaten away'.
Q5 Cola can damage teeth, so drink less of it and clean your teeth regularly.

Physical Processes

Page 55 — Static Charge

Q1 Rub the rod with the duster very quickly.
Q2 negative
Q3

Charge 1	Charge 2	Force between
positive	positive	repel
positive	negative	attract
negative	positive	attract
negative	negative	repel

Q4 a) closed
b) open
c) Discharge, e.g. touching the plate or bringing a radiation source close to plate.

Page 56 — Electricity and Current

Q1 a conductor
Q2 an insulator
Q3 The following should be ticked:
copper, steel, brass, aluminium
Q4 Electric current is a flow of **charge**. It flows from **negative** to **positive**. Conventional current flows from **positive** to **negative**. For current to flow, a **power source** and a **complete circuit** are needed. The current flowing out of a battery is **the same as** the current flowing back into it.
Q5 The following should be ticked:

Metal Strip

Page 57 — Electric Current in Circuits

Q1

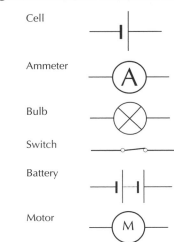

Cell

Ammeter

Bulb

Switch

Battery

Motor

The Answers

Q2   kinetic energy
Q3 a)   4A
  b)   2A
  c)   the second circuit
Q4   It is when electricity finds a path of lower resistance to flow through.

Page 58 — Magnets and Electromagnets

Q1   E.g. iron, nickel, cobalt
Q2

Q3

or N-S, N-S

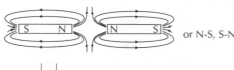

or N-S, S-N

Q4

Page 59 — Force and Movement

Q1   Speed = Distance / Time
Q2   speed up (accelerate), slow down (decelerate), change shape, change direction, begin to rotate
Q3   Forces are measured in **newtons**. An unbalanced force is needed to **start something** moving. If all forces are balanced a moving object will **keep going**. Weight is a type of **force** and is measured in **newtons**.
Q4 a)

  b)   Lynda and Spot fall to left and right respectively.

Page 60 — Air Resistance and Friction

Q1

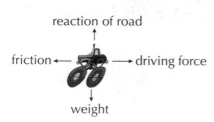

  a)   the driving force
  b)   Slow it down until the car stops.

Q2 a)

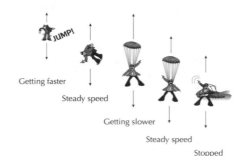

  b)   The drag force is the same in both cases.

Page 61 — Force and Rotation

Q1

Q2   When you are using a lever, the longer the lever on your side of the pivot the **greater** the turning force about the pivot. Using a long lever with the pivot close to the load makes lifting a large load **easier**. Using a long lever with the pivot close to the load makes the distance moved by the load **small**.

Q3   **A**

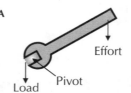

      B

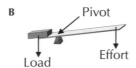

      C

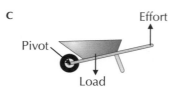

Page 62 — Pressure

Q1 a)   increase
  b)   The speed will be higher.
  c)   Narrow. A pointy end has a smaller surface area so will exert a greater pressure on the target.
Q2   Little Foot's feet are smaller so exert more pressure than the feet of Big Foot, even though Big Foot weighs more.

The Answers

Page 63 — Properties of Light

Q1 Light always travels in **straight** lines.

Q2

Q3 Light rays from a source can be blocked, creating a region where there is no light — a shadow.

Q4

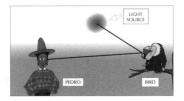

Page 64 — Reflection

Q1 a)

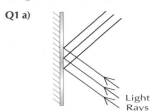

b) mirror

Q2 a)

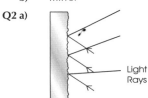

b) E.g. paper, brick wall
c) diffuse
Q3 E.g. preening yourself, cars (rear view), periscopes

Page 65 — Refraction

Q1 a substance that a wave travels through
Q2 refraction
Q3 a)

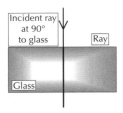

b)

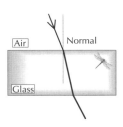

Q4 a) When a light ray travels from one medium into another, more dense, medium, it bends **towards** the normal.
b) When a light ray travels from one medium into another, less dense, medium, it bends **away from** the normal.

Page 66 — Colour

Q1 a) dispersion
b) spectrum
c) The following should be ticked:
yellow, red, green, indigo, blue, violet, orange
Q2 a) red
b) A red filter will transmit red light but will absorb all the rest.

Page 67 — Sound

Q1 a) When air is sucked out of the jar the ringing of the alarm clock inside the jar gets **quieter**. When all the air is removed the bell **cannot be heard**.
b) There is no air in the jar to carry the vibrations.
Q2 E.g. reflection, refraction
Q3 a) 1
b) i)

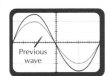

ii) louder sound

Page 68 — Hearing

Q1 **Ruler** vibrates.
Ear **drum** vibrates.
Ear **bones** vibrate.
Hairs vibrate in the **cochlea** sending a message to the **brain**.
Q2 a) old man
b) So dolphins can hear one another. / High frequencies travel better underwater than low frequencies.
c) Dolphins can hear higher frequency sounds than dogs. This means that dolphins can hear sounds of a **higher pitch**.

Page 69 — The Moon and Satellites

Q1 An object in orbit about a planet.
Q2 The following should be ticked:
The Moon, The Hubble Space Telescope
Q3 E.g. communication, monitoring the weather
Q4 gravity

Q5

The Answers

Q6 The **Moon** orbits the Earth in **28** days. The Moon appears to change **shape** as it goes through a full orbit of the Earth. This is because we only see the part of the Moon which is **reflecting** light from the Sun. We see **different** amounts of the Moon's sunny side as it orbits the Earth — that's why it seems to change shape because you can't see the **dark** bits.

Page 70 — Day and Night

Q1 a) and b)

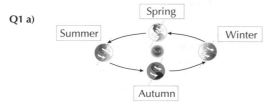

c) 24 hours

Q2 The Earth rotates, bringing the Sun into view at different parts of the Earth at different times.

Q3 a) in the east

b) noon

Page 71 — The Four Seasons

Q1 a)

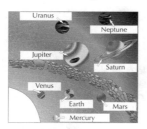

b) i) summer

ii) The Sun generally appears higher during the day (around noon, say).

Q2 At high latitudes, sunlight is still spread out over more ground than at the equator. So the ground at the equator will heat up more during the day, and the climate will be warmer.

Pages 72-73 — The Solar System

Q1 a planet

Q2 a star

Q3 A star is a luminous light source whereas a planet does not emit its own light.

Q4

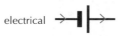

Q5 orbit

Q6 ellipse

Q7 gravity

Q8 a) Mercury

b) Jupiter

c) Mercury

d) Neptune

e) The orbit time of planets **increases** as the distance from the Sun increases.

Q9 Mars and Jupiter

Q10 Comets, Asteroids, Planets, Moons

Page 74 — Types of Energy and Energy Transfer

Q1

 light

 electrical

 sound

kinetic

heat

gravitational potential

 elastic potential

chemical

Q2

energy input   useful energy output   wasted energy

no

Page 75 — Energy Resources

Q1 a) fossil fuel

b) wind power

c) chemical (batteries)

d) chemical (wood)

e) wave power

Page 76 — Generating Electricity

Q1 a) Any three of, e.g. oil, coal, gas, wood

b) oil, coal and gas — non-renewable
wood — renewable

c) Petrol is too expensive and valuable.

Q2 E.g. be more energy efficient. Use renewable sources of energy.

Q3 solar, wind, wave, wood (or biomass)

Q4 e.g. wood

SFW30M